THE EGO TRAP

Twenty-two years of following her diplomat father around the world had left Romy yearning for peace and security, so inheriting her great-aunt's cabin in California was a Godsend—except the scheming Chase O'Donoghue seemed to have been sent with it!

THE EGO TRAP

BY

ELIZABETH OLDFIELD

MILLS & BOON LIMITED
15-16 BROOK'S MEWS
LONDON W1A 1DR

First published 1984
Australian copyright 1984
Philippine copyright 1984
This edition 1984

© Elizabeth Oldfield 1984

ISBN 0 263 74797 2

Set in Monophoto Plantin 11 on 11 pt.
01–1084 – 50647

Made and printed in Great Britain by
Richard Clay (The Chaucer Press) Ltd,
Bungay, Suffolk

CHAPTER ONE

MORNING mist rolled off the Pacific—white shimmering mist which drifted around the multi-storeyed office blocks, the concrete needles, the soaring skyline of San Francisco like so much cotton wool protecting porcelain towers. The August air was chill and damp. Tourists shivered in fleecy-lined jackets as they photographed what was reputed to be the Golden Gate Bridge, though only the tips of the highest stanchions could be seen where mist dissolved and china blue sky began. To the north the coastline was shrouded. Fog seeped through groves of massive redwoods, its moisture gently nourishing them—the tallest trees on earth. Here, within easy driving distance of the city's bustle of sophistication, there was tranquillity. The landscape was hauntingly dramatic; beneath the cloud blanket lay rocky headlands and silent grassy coves where surf pounded on coarse-sand shores.

With a sigh of relief, Romy MacDonald swung off the State Highway. Unfamiliar with left-hand drive cars and American motoring norms, the added nuisance value of the fog had turned her first excursion to San Francisco into an ordeal, but now, thank goodness, it was almost over. That morning she had risen with the dawn, intent on beating the rush-hour traffic, but her plans had gone awry. Despite one eye glued to the map, a six-lane freeway, heading heaven knows where, had scooped her up and she had had to motor for miles in the wrong direction before managing to escape.

When she had hit the city, the commuting cars had reminded her of lemmings, scampering hither and thither intent on destruction—hers! To make matters worse, the famous hills did, indeed, resemble the summits and plunges of a roller-coaster, and Romy had driven with heart in mouth and bloodless knuckles, terrified the brakes might fail and the hired Buick would scream headlong into the fathomless depths of San Francisco Bay. Parking had also been a problem. Level streets appeared to be banned by law, so she had had to settle for an incline, but despite front wheels carefully slanted towards the kerb, her shopping trip had been fraught. Was she in an authorised parked area? Would the car be safe? Had she overlooked some time restriction?

Now her troubles were evaporating and Romy smiled, tucking a strand of glossy red hair into her higgledy-piggledy topknot. On balance the morning had been successful. She had neither crashed nor collected a parking ticket and behind her the seat was piled high with shelf paper, packets of detergent, scouring powder and gallons and gallons of white gloss paint. Regrettably her shopping list languished in solitary splendour on the kitchen table so she had had to buy from memory, but she was certain the bulk of the essentials had been acquired. Romy cast a quick glance over her shoulder. In addition to the cleaning and painting gear there were two gigantic flagons of disinfectant, fresh fruit and a brown paper carrier bursting with her purchases from a health food store.

Country road petered out into dirt track. The poor visibility meant it would be hard to spot the narrow turn down to the bay and Romy's brow furrowed as she tried to pick out recognisable landmarks. Driving alone in the mist was an eerie sensation, like being the sole survivor after a nuclear blast, and she fiddled with the radio, searching for sounds to fill the empty air. Hand on the dial, she was swithering between a disc jockey's blurb and rock music when the lane unexpectedly dipped into a sharp bend. Steep grassy banks dotted with wild flowers loomed on either side, making her outlook even more indistinct.

Romy gave a bleat of dismay. A figure was powering out of the mist, a man in grey tee-shirt and shorts. He was running towards her, head down, directly into the path of the car, seemingly engrossed in a world of his own. Batting at every knob and switch in a frantic attempt to locate the horn, which she knew had to be somewhere, she resorted to yells.

'Look out, you silly fool!' she shrieked, at an eardrum-splitting pitch of decibels.

It was obvious he could never hear her, but maybe the approaching growl of the Buick's engine managed to pierce his reverie, for abruptly his head snapped up. Their eyes met in cold panic—Romy's wide and green, the man's a startled blue. For a split second he froze, not knowing how to escape, and she slammed her foot down hard. There was a horrifying screech as the car skidded, churning up deep furrows in the earth. Romy heard a series of thuds, the protest of suspension, and was battered when her purchases shot over from the back seat to cascade

around her like falling rocks. At the edge of her
vision the runner disappeared into the undergrowth—a blur of arms, legs and terror writ
large. She wrenched at the wheel, clawing for
control as the car became a frenzied metal
monster, bumping and lurching against the bank.
Several careening yards further on, Romy
managed to bring the Buick to a halt. She sat,
pale faced and trembling, catching in harsh gulps
of air as she summoned up the strength to climb
out and face the consequences. Everything had
happened in seconds. Had she hit the man? Her
heart pounded. Oh heavens! maybe he was lying
like a rag doll with shattered limbs and blood
pulsing from his wounds. Biting into an index
finger to stem her dismay, she hobbled back
along the track on rubber legs.

When she rounded the corner her insides
turned over with gratitude, for she saw that the
runner was propped up against the bank, tenderly
inspecting a tanned calf muscle. He looked fit and
strong, all in one piece. Blades of grass were
clinging to his clothes and sticking out of his
curly black hair, but they were the only evidence
of his frenetic leap for safety.

'Are you okay?' Romy asked, her smile a
tremulous mixture of hope and encouragement.

Looking up, he spiked her with stormy blue
eyes. 'No, I'm damn well not. My leg took one
helluva knock, thanks to you, and I'm sick to
death of folk treating these roads like a Grand
Prix circuit!'

'But I don't——' she began to protest, eager to
explain that she had only recently arrived in
California, but her voice faded when she saw he
was not listening. After several more cossetting

strokes, he inspected a diver's watch strapped to his broad wrist and glowered at her.

'Do you realise what you've done?' he demanded, the blue eyes thrusting out like lasers beneath thick dark lashes.

Romy gulped. Maybe one of those sturdy brown legs *was* broken? 'What?' she asked faintly, fearing the worst.

'You've loused up my jogging schedule.'

Her brows peaked in astonishment. 'Your jogging schedule?' Hysterical laughter bubbled, but she swallowed it down. Here she was, terrified that she had condemned him to a wheelchair for life, and all he cared about was some tuppeny-halfpenny morning run. He must be a fitness freak *ad nauseum*! 'I'm terribly sorry,' she said, trying hard to sound concerned.

'So you should be.' He rose to his feet, making a laborious show of brushing himself off. He was tall, with wide shoulders and narrow hips, in his early thirties at a guess, and very cross. 'This stretch of coast used to be real peaceful, but it's getting more like Disneyland every day. I've had people picnicking in my meadow *and* hikers knocking on the door to ask directions.' When he saw she was wondering how this could be relevant, he jammed his lips together and produced the punchline. 'And the roads are full of maniacs *like you*!'

Having ascertained he was intact, Romy could reconsider the situation. 'You were running straight into the path of my car and not looking where you were going,' she informed him with chocolate-coated civility. 'There is such a thing as road sense.'

He placed his hands on his hips, long fingers spread wide, and leaned towards her. 'I was on the correct side,' he snarled.

Such open hostility ignited a spark of temper and
Romy made one of her grand flamenco gestures.
'Oh, no, you weren't.'

'Think!' he ordered. She did and her face fell.
For a moment back there, Romy remembered, she
had reverted to habit. '*You* were the one who was
on the wrong side,' he taunted.

'I'm terribly sorry.' She was too rattled by the
smug satisfaction at the mistake being hers to
bother making the apology genuine.

'You're English,' he accused, suspicious eyes
raking over her curvy frame in the pink velour
jumpsuit as though he expected to discover a
'Made in England' tag. 'So that's how you come
to be driving on the wrong side of the road! What
are you, a secret weapon sent over by MI5 to
pick off the entire population of the States one by
one?'

Romy bristled. Trust her to find a racist!
Without exception the Americans she had met in
the past had been friendly, fussing over her
accent. The males had fussed even more over her
heart-shaped face and torrent of striking red hair,
but today it was her misfortune to discover a hick
who did not give a damn about furthering Anglo-
American relationships.

'I'm a Scot,' she told him, eyes blazing
emerald fire.

'Never! I can tell one U.K. accent from
another and you, kiddo, never came from
Scotland.'

Romy was in no mood to explain her mixed-up
background to a stranger. 'Hard luck, but I do,
kiddo!' she spat.

'Suit yourself.'

'I will.'

A thick dark brow lifted, but a moment later he lost interest and was back to making a keen inspection of his watch. As though under orders from a mystical starter, his powerful limbs tensed and on the muttered chant of, 'One, two, three,' he leapt forward. Seconds later he had been swallowed up by the mist.

Abandoned, Romy stomped down the track to the Buick and wrenched open the door. 'Oh no!' she wailed as the smell of pine hit her. A screw cap had leaked, and the front seats and floor were swimming in greeny-yellow disinfectant. She waved a fist in frustration. 'That damn jogger,' she grumbled, blaming all her troubles on him.

It took nearly a full box of brand new tissues to mop up the liquid, and Romy's mood blackened even further when, on resuming her journey, she discovered she *had* missed the lane. Battling to switch the big car around, her intended three-point turn became a hectic seven, and by the time she pulled up alongside the cabin's tumble-down fence she felt like a wet rag. The day had started on a burst of enthusiasm but now she wanted to howl. Her father had warned that she could be embarking on a wild goose chase, but she had been so convinced that it was her destiny to leave England and Peter, and make a fresh start in California, that she had not listened.

'I agree that, on the face of it, being left a house sounds pretty exciting, but if I know Prudence there'll be some drawback,' her father had prophesied, puffing at his cigar.

'Don't be a spoilsport,' she had chided. 'The timing is superb. Yesterday news of Great-aunt Prudence's bequest came out of the blue, and this afternoon my boss warned I should be on the lookout for another job because the company is having to cut down on staff. Being last in, I'll be first out.'

'Pretty secretaries who can spell are in great demand, you can easily find something else.'

Romy had had to agree, but persisted with her reading of the situation. 'I still believe fate has lent a hand.' She did not tell her father that Peter had chosen the previous evening to propose—another reason for heading West!

Mr MacDonald had pulled a face. 'Fate's hand can pack a nasty punch,' he had warned. 'You can bet your bottom dollar there'll be some snag. Prudence was an eccentric, even thirty years ago. I never could understand what possessed Uncle Alex to marry her, because she always reminded me of Medusa. You know, so hideous that all those who looked upon her were petrified.'

'That's not very charitable!'

'You never met her.'

'Pa, she can't have been that bad. Besides, most of our family tend to be a touch eccentric, even if their looks don't turn people to stone. Take you for example.' Romy had grinned at the portly man with his silver mutton-chop whiskers and scarlet cravat.

'Me?' he had chuckled. 'I'm just your friendly neighbourhood diplomat.'

'You're a rolling stone, and I've been hauled along as excess baggage ever since I can remember. I collected stamps in my passport like other children collected autographs. But no more. Now I have a chance to settle down in a home of my own.' Her eyes had grown misty.

'Why not tell Peter you're fancying domesticity?' her father had suggested slyly, but had changed tack when he saw her expression. 'Bah! what do you want to settle down for? You're only a girl. Look at me, I'm approaching sixty and still on the hoof, and I hope I always will be. Only stick-in-the-muds are content to stay put. You'll soon be fed up, just you wait and see.'

Right now, Romy *was* fed up, and she had been in the States for less than a week. As she unloaded her battered and bruised purchases, she stopped to glower at the timber-built cabin she had inherited. Cabin was too grand a description, 'shack' was more appropriate. On the flight over she had sketched mind pictures of a pretty little bungalow with roses trailing around the door and cropped green lawns, but the first glimpse had brought her down to earth with a bump. Once upon a time the shack may have made a decent home, but now it was in the final throes of decay. Great-aunt Prudence had not been one of the 'House & Garden' brigade, that much was certain. The interior decoration was in dire need of renewal and paint had flaked in great patches from the outer walls, leaving the resultant bare wood to be bleached pale by the salt air. Instead of neat lawns, the surrounding garden was a choked green labyrinth which had not felt the caress of secateurs or mower for years. Staggering up the two steps to the verandah, a paint can in each hand, Romy gave a terse little laugh. The bored lawyer, who had explained her great-aunt's will, had mentioned superb sea views, but to date all the mist had allowed was one brief blue flash, as if to quash any doubts about the Pacific lying a few hundred yards from her front door.

She could not prevent a shudder when she entered the living-room. Great-aunt Prudence

had kept cats. Cats which must have lain on the
beds, sprayed in the corners and prowled amidst
the jungle garden in the understandable misap-
prehension they were wild tigers in Africa.
Fragrance of feline was the perfume of the day,
every day. It had soaked into the rugs, the
floorboards, the very fabric of the building.
Ignoring the cold, damp mist, Romy had left the
windows open wide from morning until night,
and had thrust everything washable into the
ancient twin-tub in the kitchen. This afternoon,
with the aid of what remained of the disinfectant,
she intended to undertake a marathon wipe-
down, in the hope that tabby could be persuaded
to give way to pine.

Her trips back and forth to the car were almost
complete when the telephone rang, a shrill
sentinel which accentuated the quietness. This
could only be Mrs Klein, her great-aunt's sister,
a gloomy lady with iron-grey hair twisted into a
torturous figure of eight, who had as little time
for Prudence deceased as she had apparently had
for Prudence alive.

'Are you safe?' she enquired, making Romy
smile. Mrs Klein equated living in the cabin with
living in Timbuktu, and had phoned every day
since her arrival to ask the same question. This
was kind, as they were virtually strangers, but her
disapproval of the shack and Romy's decision to
live there, remained a strong undertone.

'I'm fine, thank you. I've been out and bought
paint, so now I'm all set for action.'

Mrs Klein made a derisory sucking sound.
'You'll never douse the smell of those cats, no
matter how much paint you splash on. Jim and I
had the dreadful creatures put to sleep the day

Prudence died, and not a moment too soon! Silly old broad,' she chided, showing a marked lack of sisterly affection. 'Fancy living out there with a houseful of stinking cats. I just hope we managed to round them all up.'

'I haven't seen any strays, but with this mist I haven't seen much of anything,' Romy confessed.

Mrs Klein proved she was a skilled exponent at the art of a damper putting. 'There isn't much to see, just fields and ocean. The bay is off the beaten track, and the guy who occupies the house above you works abroad, so he's rarely home. Not that he's much of a neighbour when he is around. As I explained, there's a long history of bad blood between him and Prudence. When Alex was alive things were different, but after he passed on Prudence went completely nuts. She was never the easiest of people to get along with.' A terse laugh indicated an understatement, and Mrs Klein set off in a different direction. 'If you get bored, I guess you could always come and stay with us in Oakland.'

Romy refused the low-key invitation. After her tussle with the traffic and the angry jogger, staying put was infinitely preferable to risking the roads again right now, and she had work to do. Besides, before coming out to the cabin she had spent two nights with the Kleins and had discovered too many gaps—gaps of generation, beliefs, preferences. At first she had wondered if the old couple resented her falling heir to the cabin, but had soon learned of their relief at escaping the trauma of dealing with Prudence's shabby domain. They had greeted her at San Francisco's International Airport, asking polite questions about her father whom they vaguely remembered from the dim and distant past, but had been unable to conceal that they considered her to be an alien in their world. Very generously, they had taken her to see the lawyer who was handling her great-aunt's estate, and had later helped to organise a hire car and provisions, but through it all they could not understand what motivated a young woman to take on an old cabin, filled with an assortment of down-at-heel furniture.

'Sell up,' Jim Klein had advised, half an eye on the ever-flickering. television screen. 'I can't imagine who'd want to buy the cabin, but I guess the land must be worth something. I seem to remember Alex had some guy who was interested.' He thought for a moment, scratching his head. 'Nah, that was years ago.'

'I'm not looking for a buyer,' Romy had pointed out.

When there was a commercial break, Mrs Klein joined in. 'But the place is so basic!' she had protested. 'Okay, the phone is installed, but that's all. You're really back to nature out there. You don't have television, or paved roads, or street lighting, and apart from that one absent neighbour, there's no other house in sight. You won't be able to gossip, or pop round to the corner shop.'

'I don't mind,' Romy had replied with a smile, but she realised the Kleins had marked her down as an eccentric—like Great-aunt Prudence. Well, maybe she was!

Chase O'Donoghue took a swig of ice-cold Budweiser beer and wiped the froth from his mouth with the back of his hand. 'Mmm, the first one always tastes extra special.' He took a second gulp. 'Even if I manage to find a Bud when I'm abroad, it never tastes the same as it does at home.'

His companion grinned. 'Good to be back, eh? You've had one helluva stretch away this time. What was it—five months?'

'Six. Still, at least it means there's a longer break than usual. I have an eight week repat ahead.'

'Lucky you,' Stu Beazley commented.

'Yeah, it's great to see the bay again.' Chase said automatically, then his blue eyes clouded. 'Well no, that's wrong because I haven't seen it! What in the hell's happening with the weather right now?' He shook his dark head in bewilderment. 'Okay, maybe in July there's some mist, but even then the ridge tends to screen the bay and it's fragmented. Come mid-morning, the air is clear. I swear I can't ever remember it hanging around at this time of year.' He frowned down into his glass. 'The damn weather bugs me, and so do other things.'

'Like what?'

Stu took a swig of his own beer and relaxed, smiling at the man opposite. He was delighted to see Chase again, eager to hear an account of his latest assignment in the Middle East. As a deep-sea diver, Chase worked all over the world and Stu feasted off his reminiscences of far-off lands and exotic locations, though he never wished to swap roles. Stu had been born and bred in a San Francisco commuter suburb, moving only another fifteen miles out when he had married. The urge to broaden his horizons had never come and he was content with his life as an attorney, working

from an office overlooking San Francisco Bay, a
view so familiar he considered he owned a part
share. Stu enjoyed the familiar. He cast a fond
look around the rustic living-room with its pale
carpet, chocolate-brown leather chairs, golden
curtains, and the touches of smocked cushions
and embroidered work where Ginette had
stamped her personality. He counted up his
blessings. His wife was an imaginative home-
maker, a good mother, a loving partner, and he
would not have traded her and their two children
for Chase's lifestyle, no matter how exciting or
lucrative. His thoughts went to Julia, the young
woman who normally made up the foursome at
these welcome-home dinners. Julia was an up-
and-coming executive with an important advertising agency, but this evening business matters
had detained her. Stu wondered how Chase felt
about Julia putting business first. Maybe he
didn't care.

The curly-haired Californian sprawled a den-
imed leg over the arm of his chair. 'My jogging's
bugging me,' he grumbled. 'In the past I've picked
up my exercise times precisely where I left off, but
yesterday I was way down the shute and——'

'You know why that is, don't you?' Ginette
intervened, coming back from the kitchen where
she had been checking on the state of the meal.

Chase eyed her cautiously. Stu sympathised
with his grievances, but Ginette had a tendency
to mock. 'Why?' he challenged.

'Whether you like it or not, Chase, you're
middle-aged,' she pronounced and received a
look of thunder. 'Three score years and ten
makes thirty-five middle-aged. From now on, it's
downhill all the way.'

'Gee, thanks!'

'On the other hand, I suppose you should be happy that now you can run for President.'

'Gee, thanks,' he said again.

Ginette was a pain. She was thirty-five too, yet he didn't make a point of telling *her* the days were numbered. The trouble was he knew that his hostess did not give a damn about growing old; she was so wrapped up in her kids and Stu, attending self-improvement workshops or dashing to classes on vegetable carving, that age was immaterial. Ginette plonked herself down beside Stu on the sofa and reached for her crochetwork. With solid hips, firmly sketched features and strong opinions, she had an ageless quality. Probably she would look the same all her life, he thought, remembering her as a matronly fourteen!

'And is the bachelor boy happy to continue riding the range on his ownsome?' she enquired, employing an air of neutrality which left Chase undecided as to whether she was making amicable conversation or sarcastically condemning him, once again.

'Yes,' he said, then took a chance at honesty. 'But even after two years, it feels odd to come back to an empty house. I don't like it. The day-to-day mechanics of living are no problem but I have to admit I miss Paddy's company, even our rows!'

This was one of those rare occasions when Ginette thought she could detect a streak of vulnerability in Chase's makeup and a traitorous urge rose to mother him, though mostly she would have rather *smothered* him! He could be an arrogant son of a bitch. She cast a sidelong glance at her guest. By film star standards Chase was not good-looking, his jaw was too strong, his features a little too irregular, but he had sex appeal. He was also good with kids, handy around the house and a skilled cook. Yet despite his efficiency with matters domestic, he was intensely masculine—a man's man. To Ginette he represented a paradox on two legs. She gave a silent groan. What a waste! There he sat, perfect husband material and yet completely self-sufficient.

'Is it my imagination or are you starting to sound English?' she mused, as he and Stu discussed his latest assignment. 'Some of your expressions sound real English to me.'

Chase shrugged broad shoulders. 'It's possible. I'm out of the States far more than I'm in, and one of my best buddies is an English diver, so maybe I'm picking up the lingo from him.'

Stu asked a question about the Middle East, but when there was a gap in the conversation, Ginette took her chance. 'Isn't it about time you stopped running and married Julia?' she asked, ignoring her husband's warning glance. 'You two guys have been a couple for long enough.'

Expecting some such stab, Chase happily girded himself for battle. 'Be honest, don't you mean that as I've been sleeping with Julia for the past seven years, it's high time I make an honest woman out of her?' he attacked with bravura rudeness.

His opponent could give as good as she got. 'I sure do! You breeze back to California every blue moon, and there's old Julia patiently waiting. I reckon she deserves a long-service medal, in addition to a band of gold.'

Chase took another mouthful of beer. 'What

makes you think she's interested in getting hitched?' he enquired laconically.

'Because she's thirty-three and she dotes on you. Though why any woman would want to latch on to a guy who's away from home nine months out of every year, beats me.' Ginette cast him a wry glance. 'I bet she was waiting to pick you up from the airport?'

'She arrived twenty minutes late, delayed at the office.' He sounded mortally offended. 'Ever since her promotion last year it's been all go. I reckon she's turning into a workaholic, but then, Julia's always been hooked on her career.'

'Don't you believe it,' Ginette scoffed. In her opinion, the softly-spoken blonde *must* have other priorities. Deep down didn't every woman yearn for a husband, home and family? Ginette had no doubt that the independence the young woman flaunted was egg-shell thin. Let Chase propose, and Julia would gallop off to buy her wedding dress and veil the same day!

Chase fingered the heavy gold link chain around his neck, deciding he had no wish to become *too* embroiled in the usual argument about matrimony because Julia's attitude was something else which was bugging him. He respected the fact that she loved her job, but there were limits!

'I was almost mown down alive this morning by some loony bird in a Buick,' he complained, changing the subject. 'It turned out she came from the U.K. and was driving on the wrong side of the road. To avoid being smashed into strawberry jam, I had to leap on to the bank. I bumped my leg and that loused up any chance of meeting my training schedule.'

'Poor Chase,' soothed Ginette syrupy, and received an impatient glance.

'The area around the bay has enough visitors without importing the damn British,' he continued.

'Don't get carried away, it's not that crowded,' Stu said in protest as he rose to fetch fresh cans of beer.

Chase refused to admit he was exaggerating. 'Belive me, everywhere you go, you come across camper vans or kids marching around with packs on their backs. The mailman told me a windsurfing operation has been set up further along the coast, so I guess it won't be long before my bay is crowded with beach bums.'

'*Your* bay?' jibed Ginette. 'But it's not your bay.'

'He's using poetic licence,' Stu said, handing over a second Budweiser. He often took on the role of peace-keeper because he knew his wife and Chase of old. One false word and they could be at each other's throats. Mind you, Stu suspected they enjoyed a certain frisson when the sparks flew, for Ginette was eager to have Chase round whenever he was at home, and her invitations were always accepted!

'The bay's nearly mine, apart from old Prudence's eyesore,' Chase remarked sourly.

Ginette pushed her crochetwork away into a white linen bag. 'Mrs MacDonald has as much right to be there as you.'

He rounded on her. 'Like hell! It was settled years ago that when her husband croaked she'd quit the property and give Paddy first chance to buy. Though it's some property—half a dozen planks of rotting timber and an acre of wilderness.'

'So she changed her mind.' Ginette rose, intent on checking the final preparations for dinner. 'It's understandable that an old lady might prefer to stay put.'

'What, alone for ten years? It's dangerous for her to live under those conditions, she'd be far better off in a home where she could be properly cared for. She's gaga, Ginette. I haven't seen her yet since I've been home, thanks to the mist, but she puts the fear of God into you. She's like one of the witches from Macbeth, all flowing white hair and cackling voice. I booted one of her damn cats off my land a while back and, hell! the abuse.'

Unimpressed, Ginette pulled a face and disappeared.

'Are you still having problems with the cats?' Stu asked.

'I haven't caught sight of a single one so far,' Chase admitted grudgingly. 'Even the smell has disappeared, though I expect that's because the mist has prevented it wafting up to me. I don't understand why the old broad persists in living there,' he complained, returning to his theme. 'It would be so much easier for everyone if she moved nearer her sister in Oakland, but what does she do?' He appealed to his friend, though they both knew the answer because Chase was covering old ground. 'She turns up her nose at the series of generous offers my father and I have made over the years, and sits it out in that monstrosity of a hut.'

'Keep your fingers crossed that a hearse'll roll down the hill one of these days,' Stu joked ghoulishly. 'The old girl must be cracking on for eighty.'

'She'll outlive me,' Chase mumbled darkly. 'I'll never be able to have my diving ranch.' His thoughts went to the plans he and Paddy, his father, had first formulated years ago whereby they would absorb Prudence MacDonald's property and establish a centre for underwater sports in the bay. The old woman's cabin sat below his stone and timber spread, to the left of the communal lane, and on the flattest area—the area designated to take the large rectangular swimming pool which would form the hub of the whole scheme. But his plans were pipedreams and looked like remaining that way, because this far the cantankerous Mrs MacDonald had refused to budge. 'Everything is planned down to the last tile, but what wasn't planned was Prudence's cussedness! It wouldn't be worthwhile sending another offer, would it?' he asked hopefully, for Stu handled all his legal affairs.

'Waste of time. She never bothers to answer her mail.'

'Couldn't we approach through her lawyers? Get some brave soul to go and see her?' Chase gave a bark of bleak amusement. 'There's no point me trying to open negotiations, she hates my guts. She'd probably set the cats on me.'

Stu shook his head. 'I don't even know who's dealing with her affairs right now. There was some bust-up with the last firm and they washed their hands of her, but she'll never sell. You know that.'

'I guess so.' He heaved a sigh, accepting he had reached the end of the trail. 'I spent most of the afternoon sorting a fitment in my hot tub which had jammed while I was away. What a job!'

Ginette had returned to usher them into the

dining-room. 'More grumbles?' she rebuked, brown eyes dancing. 'You know your trouble, Chase? You're heading for the male menopause.'

Remembering the description next morning, Chase gave a rueful grin. If it wasn't so ridiculous, he would have been tempted to agree, though agreeing with Ginette went against the grain. But he was no longer down in the dumps, because the mist had shredded, at long last, and there were sparkling glimpses of the ocean as he jogged along. When he reached his mailbox, official finishing point on the six mile run, he discovered he was fifty seconds faster than required and stood, panting happily, as the blue and white mail van pulled up alongside. He collected his envelopes and exchanged some lighthearted banter with the driver, a long-standing chum.

'How does it feel to have the bay all to yourself?' the man asked, and chuckled when Chase's dark brows pulled together. 'Haven't you heard? Old Mrs MacDonald died nearly three months ago.'

'She did?' He was astonished.

'Yup. Mrs Klein came out and found the old gal bad with bronchitis. She whipped her off to hospital, but two days later she kicked it.'

Chase grinned as the realisation of what this could mean began to filter through. He wanted to give a whoop of delight, but restrained himself to a chuckle. Old Prudence had had a good innings, and he had never liked the old shrew anyway, so why be hypocritical and pretend to mourn? His plans for the diving ranch began to light up like neon in his mind. Now he had a future!

'So what's happened about her house and land?' he enquired eagerly.

The mailman was a walking information centre, who considered that spreading gossip around his district was a vital part of his services, and he leant comfortably against his van to tell the tale.

'I imagine everything will have been left to Mrs Klein. She seems to have taken charge. She came out and had all the cats rounded up and put to sleep. No one else has been near, as far as a I know.' He shrugged. 'Neither her nor Prudence had any kids so I expect the place'll be put on the market the minute the legalities have been cleared.'

'Mrs Klein won't want to hang on.' Chase had met the old lady occasionally, and well remembered her distaste for her sister's lifestyle.

'Never,' the mailman agreed. 'She's a city bird. She reckons your bay is at the back of beyond.'

'Do you know if she ever comes out here to check on the place? I'd like to get in touch, but I don't have her address,' he explained. 'I've been desperate to get my hands on that land for years.'

'I haven't seen her recently. I've been stashing the odd item away in the mailbox, but nothing's been collected for a long while so maybe she's due soon. You'll just have to keep your eyes open and hope to catch her.'

'Will do. She's bound to turn up one of these days.'

Delighted with his morning's detective work, Chase bade a hasty farewell and hurled himself down the hill and into his house.

'Guess what?' he crowed, when he had dialled the office of Stuart M. Beazley and Associates.

'At long last Prudence MacDonald has obliged me by shuffling off this mortal coil! Send out an offer, Stu, at the price we agreed. Address it to the sister, Mrs Klein, at the bay here, though if I should see her in the meantime I'll mention it personally.' He could not stop grinning. 'I know she'll be delighted to sell me the property. Isn't it great? That cabin and land are going to be mine now and, Stu, old buddy, they represent my ticket to a wonderful future!'

CHAPTER TWO

ROMY crawled out of bed and stretched cat-like, before sagging abruptly with a groan. Yesterday, between sessions hung over the twin-tub, a trial experiment had revealed that the cabin's pine-planked floor, so far only brushed, responded well to soap and water. On hands and knees, she had set to work. After two hours' scrubbing, the living-room had so delighted her that she had grabbed a handful of sultanas in the name of a meal, and started on the kitchen. Later both bedrooms had received the same treatment and though it was dusk, she had then emerged to scrub the verandah. By nightfall her hands were a wrinkled red, her legs weak and her back cemented into a painful curve, but despite feeling a hundred years old, her smile was wide.

How different the rooms looked when she replaced freshly-shampooed rugs in terra cotta and white. Now clean pale green curtains swung at spotless windows, and surely the smell of cats had diminished? The cabin was on its way to being transformed and given her determination, plus leafy pot plants on the sills and a rearrangement of the furniture, the end result promised to be charming. Having her visions to spur her on, Romy brimmed with enthusiasm once more.

Sitting down to breakfast seemed a waste of time, so she stood on the verandah in her cerise satin happicoat, a slice of cantaloupe melon in one hand, a tumbler of fresh orange juice in the other. For the first time since her arrival, the air was completely clear. The blanket of mist had dissolved to reveal a few thousand miles of ocean stretched out before her, topped by clear blue sky. As she basked in the warmth of the morning sun, Romy decided that although her view could never be described as superb—not compared with sights she had seen in Rio, Hong Kong and Sydney, this particular piece of-coast had its own appeal. Behind the cabin, a half-circle of green meadows formed the hilly bay. To her left, past gnarled trees, the shore was rocky, while to the right small waves lapped on a sweep of white sand which led to a distant headland. Licking melon juice from her fingers, Romy went indoors to swallow a kelp tablet which was supposed to work wonders. She marched into the bedroom, but when she swung open the door of the huge old-fashioned wardrobe, her brow creased. What should she wear?

Today was painting day, but never having painted before, and because she was the type who relied more on energy than expertise, Romy suspected she could end up covered in the stuff. Risking the designer jeans again, after yesterday's scrubbing, seemed unwise, nor was she inclined to ruin her jumpsuit. She sighed. Ninety-nine per cent of her clothes were suited to either socialising or city life. Her father made a habit of visiting boutiques whenever he remembered her existence and mailing back his purchases, but as he moved in a world of cocktail parties and foreign locations, he bought accordingly. She did not fancy wielding a paintbrush clad in an Indian kaftan or a white lace halter-neck, though only

sailors or fishermen were in viewing distance, and
they would need binoculars!

Frowning, Romy riffled through her collection
but when her hand fell on a cloth-of-silver
harem suit, she grinned. One of her father's
more extreme choices, it sported voluminous
pants, long sleeves caught into tight wristbands,
and a high neck. The outfit would make the
perfect coverall, despite bearing the tag of some
trendy fashion house. In the past she had never
been at ease decked out like a Las Vegas
concubine and it would give her great pleasure
to toss the suit away once her painting stint was
through.

She climbed out of her happicoat and into the
harem suit, not bothering with underwear
because that meant more washing, and she had
had enough of washing right now. Her hair
created a problem; strewn around her shoulders
like a fiery hurricane, it was destined to get in the
way, so she yanked up a massive handful and tied
it on top of her head with a length of string.
Ribbons were somewhere, she knew, but at
present everything was continually being shifted
around and somehow they had been mislaid.

Within minutes Romy discovered that painting
had its share of pitfalls. Opening the can proved
to be a challenge. Brute force was required and
the spoon recruited to prise off the lid bent nearly
double. She popped it back into the drawer with
the silent prayer that Great-aunt Prudence's
silver was not antique. Stepladders could not be
found, so a dining chair was requisitioned. Wary
of spoiling the red plush back and padded seat,
she smothered over yellowing sheets of the 'San
Francisco Chronicle' and then marched out to

position the chair at one end of the verandah. Paint brush in hand, Romy climbed aboard.

The chair was too low, so every time she needed to reach the top of the wall she had to stand on tiptoe. Once or twice she wobbled alarmingly, but she survived. The sun grew warmer and, combined with the stretching and her trips up and down off the chair to reload her brush, Romy became pink-faced and flustered. She bent her head to inspect a knot in the wood and felt her switch of hair smear against wet paint—so now she sported white gloss highlights!

She soldiered on until her stomach rumbled to tell her it was time for coffee and 'cookies', as the woman in the supermarket had termed the sweet biscuits she had bought, but what had happened to the cookies? Romy could not recall storing them away in the kitchen cupboard. Pensively she sucked in her lip, then her face brightened. They must still be in the car, doubtless the packet had rolled under the seat during her emergency stop to avoid that stupid jogger. Paintbrush in hand, Romy sped fleetfoot down the path, edged free the low garden gate with one knee, and peered into the depths of the Buick. Under the seat were sweet wrappers and a fire extinguisher, but no cookies. She bent for a better look.

Half-way up the hill Chase had completed his run, smug that he was one minute in hand this morning, and was on the point of unlocking the side door, when he caught a flash of silver where the lane ended at Mrs MacDonald's property. He squinted against the sunshine. Wasn't that a car parked down there? Too many people ignored the board clearly marked 'private' and headed down to the bay; some blundering there in a genuine

mistake, but others motoring on to the sand for
their barbeques. Chase was sick and tired of
clearing soft drink and beer cans away. The noise
of disgust in the back of his throat sounded like
axes grinding and he pounded downhill, intent on
turfing out the intruder. He meant to lay down
the law in no uncertain terms, but when he
rounded the corner of the fence, all he could see
was a shiny silver backside and two long silver
legs protruding from a brown car. Subconsciously
he registered that the backside was feminine and
rather cute.

'This is private property,' he growled. 'You
have no right to be here.'

His deep male voice broke into Romy's
solitude like the rumble of a cannon and she
jumped, banging her head as she leapt backwards
in surprise. She swivelled, and a fine spray of
white paint arced in midair and spattered on to
the sandy earth.

'I beg your pardon?'

'Oh, it's you. Britain's answer to the neutron
bomb.' Chase was glaring, his eyes an angry blue.
'Well, kiddo, you're back to breaking the rules.'

Recognising her antagonist, Romy glared back,
wondering if his jaw sustained a permanent
thrust. Did he march around continually baring
his fangs? Once again it was holocaust time, but
on this occasion she *knew* she was in the right.

'I'm not breaking any rules. Indeed, you're the
one who's trespassing,' she retorted, deciding to
use her snooty English lady approach. 'So if you
would be a good little boy and run all the way back
up again to the top of the hill, I'd be obliged.'

She gestured with the paintbrush as she spoke,
making Chase lurch back.

'Hell! Keep your hands still. You're lethal with that thing.' Now he had time to absorb the full effect of her appearance and his eyes widened as he surveyed the flushed cheeks, the red hair tied up with string, the opulent silver harem suit. She was a good-looking girl, yet obviously some kind of kook. 'What are you doing here?' he demanded.

Romy pushed aside an errant curl. 'I'm painting the inside of the car, what else?' she said, a naughty gleam in her eye.

'Knock it off!'

'Isn't this California where it all begins? I thought anything could become a fad out here. I'm ahead of my time, that's all, but just you wait, next year every car will have white gloss upholstery.'

'You have the wrong California,' Chase retorted. 'Maybe L.A. is packed with eccentrics, but up here we prefer old-fashioned values, one of which happens to be respect for private property.'

His holier-than-thou attitude scraped a raw nerve and Romy jolted into a fencing stance, criss-crossing the paintbrush in front of him.

'I am respecting private property and if you don't vamoosh I shall paint you, so jog off.'

'Like hell!'

Chase moved swiftly to catch hold of her wrist, but she reacted to the unexpected body contact by jerking back. The loaded brush shot out of her hand, skimmed against his tee-shirted chest, and fell to the ground with a resounding slap.

'See what you've done, you—you maniac!' wailed Romy, looking down aghast at the bristles, now thick with sand. She retrieved the brush and

straightened, shaking it aggressively. An instinct
for self-preservation made Chase lurch back, but
he was too late and a sunburst of white dots
joined the solid splash of gloss on his broad chest.

'And see what *you've* done,' he snarled,
plucking at his tee-shirt with fractious fingers.
He debated over whether to insist she pay for a
replacement, but was not too sure how she would
respond. Maybe she would start painting his
shorts? Anything seemed possible so, not wishing
to tempt fate, he contented himself with a
grumble. 'You're the maniac. First you speed
around on the wrong side of the road, and now
you sprinkle me with wet paint.' He folded his
arms, but unfolded them when he realised there
was a danger of white gloss smearing across the
tanned muscles. 'But this is private land and I
want you to leave. Or must I make you leave?'

Romy had never been able to resist a challenge,
even one from a man who was as friendly as a
firing squad.

'Make me?' Her wide green eyes glinted.
Armed with the paintbrush, she knew she was the
superior force. Her antagonist's gaze was uneasy,
he seemed fearful of what she might do next.
Turning on her heel, she marched back to the
garden gate where she announced grandly, 'We'll
see about that.'

Romy was forced to shuffle at the catch a
couple of times before it gave way, which rather
spoilt her grand exit, but nevertheless she
flounced along the path, red head held high.

'You can't go in there,' he protested, striding
after her to grab a handful of silver sleeve, though
he let go smartly enough when he saw how close
he had come to grabbing a handful of wet paint.

To his surprise Chase now noticed that the cabin's front door and windows were open wide. The girl must be living there—she was a squatter. Was nothing sacred these days? It appeared that the minute a property was left empty, some hippie moved in. He kept his eyes peeled, expecting some bushy-bearded Adonis to appear at any moment. Maybe the girl was thinking of starting up a commune here—the damn cheek! He had made a point of providing strong security for his own home against such a misfortune during his absences, but the cabin was little more than a doll's house, so gaining entry would have been easy.

'I can go in and I will. I shall telephone the police,' she announced, slashing violent patterns in the air. Predictably Chase leapt back, making Romy appreciate what she held in her hand. Lone women need no longer arm themselves with aerosols of noxious chemicals or pepper shakers to repel troublesome males—a wet paintbrush was the ultimate deterrent!

'You do that,' he said, keeping a respectable distance. 'Being British you won't know the law, but the cops will spell it out that in California people are not allowed to squat in empty houses.' She started to protest, but he held up a hand to silence her. For the first time he detected some signs of painting on the verandah. 'Even if they do try to smarten up the property,' he added. 'Though you're wasting time and money, kiddo, because this shack is on the point of being demolished.'

He sounded so positive that a tremor of doubt rippled through her. She was on unfamiliar terrain and the cabin *was* disreputable. Could a local by-law exist prohibiting properties which fell below certain standards? Romy wondered if the lawyer who had monotoned about the superb sea views kept abreast of what happened out here beyond the city boundaries? He had been a fat man with a Zapata moustache, and had made no bones about letting her know Prudence's affairs represented a troublesome triviality which he was eager to relinquish. Apparently her great-aunt had not enamoured herself, and suddenly it seemed possible that, in his rush to discard all things related to Prudence, the lawyer may only have skimmed the surface of the legalities.

'Nonsense,' she retorted in an effort to deny her impromptu fears.

'It's true.' Chase was imagining his diving ranch. The cabin would be replaced by a long low sprawl, housing changing rooms, saunas, massage facilities and a small gym, with the pool covering the major part of the unruly garden. He gave a careless laugh. 'This place is falling to bits. I'd get out of here pretty damn smart if I were you, cops or no cops. I expect the wiring's all to pot, so it has to be a fire risk, and from higher up the hill you can see that the roofing is dodgy. One good downpour and the place will be a bathtub.' Romy wondered whether he preferred her to go up in flames or drown. She told herself he was dramatising, and that she would take no notice, but he was in full spate. 'Some of the window frames are rotten and the guttering is probably choked. The old broad who lived here never had a single repair done in years. I've seen better accommodation in the ghettos of Indonesia.'

'You've been to Indonesia?' exclaimed Romy, ignoring his tale of doom. In view of what she took to be his anti-British slant, she had put him down as a small town guy, insular and bigoted. That he had travelled surprised her. She would have imagined a trip to Los Angeles was about his limit.

He nodded. 'But today it's your turn to go travelling. There are some cheap motels further down the coast, or I expect you could find a hostel.' Chase eyed her peculiar outfit, thinking that from the look of the rounded curves she was not wearing much underneath. Desire stirred, but he mentally reaffirmed that weirdos were not his type. Julia suited him. She was neat and well organised, and he approved of the way she had her life mapped out, even if she was over work-orientated right now. The red-headed creature before him, with her flapping arms and loose way with that damn paintbrush, unsettled him. He certainly didn't want *her* living in his bay. 'Southern California would suit you better,' Chase decided. 'It's all peach-fed beach boys and Hollywood and golden sunshine.'

So earnest was his dedication to having her elsewhere, that Romy needed to be flippant. 'And group sex?' she enquired, head tilted to one side.

'Mondays through Fridays. And there are ice-cream parlours shaped like elephants,' he grinned, revealing a sense of humour which surprised her. 'It's a huge holiday camp, you'd like it. Parties every night, a great chance to meet a whole bunch of interesting people, everyone a swinger.'

'Ugh!'

His grin faded. 'I beg your pardon?'

'Ugh!' Romy grimaced to emphasise her distaste. 'I've had more parties than you've had hot dinners. It's the quiet life that appeals.' Her

gaze covered the arc of white sand, the glittering
sea, the distant headland. 'This place suits me
fine.'

Chase realised a firmer approach was necessary
to make her leave. He preferred not to involve the
cops, but if he had to, he would.

'Look here, Miss——?'

'Romy, Romy MacDonald.'

'Hi, I'm Chase O'Donoghue,' he said in reflex,
speech working separately from brain, for at the
name 'MacDonald', the scenario had gone
haywire. 'You're not related to Mrs MacDonald
who lived here, are you?' he asked, as horror
struck.

'Yes.'

'What, that old bag?' he exclaimed before he
could censor it.

Prudence had been shrike voiced and hideous,
but this girl was a gem with her high cheekbones
and dancing eyes. Too *outré* for his taste, but
some guys would go a bundle on her.

Romy bridled at his harsh description. No one
was all bad and Prudence *had* left her the
property so she felt she owed her allegiance.
Gathering up as much in the way of a heated
rebuttal was tricky, in view of what she knew of
the old woman, but Romy managed to bring
something to mind.

'She was very fond of animals.'

His lip twisted. 'Trust an English girl to come
up with that one!' Chase sniffed the air. 'You'll
have realised the old gal kept cats like they were
an endangered species.'

'I'm a Scot and that's not cats, it's paint.'

He paid little heed to her protest. 'So what
gives? Why are you working on this place?' He

frowned, not caring for this dirty trick she had played on him. How long had she been here, beetling away in the mist out of sight? Chase felt he had been double-crossed. He gave her a look which had the straight line accuracy of a bullet and was just as lethal. 'You're never planning to live here, are you?' he demanded.

Romy's jaw set. He was displaying the same kind of irksome reaction as Mr and Mrs Klein, and she had had enough of negative vibes. 'I fail to see how that could be any of your business,' she rasped, and glanced down at the sandladen hairs of the brush in her hand. 'If you would excuse me, I'll go and wash this under the tap and get back to work. Don't let me detain you,' she continued sweetly. 'You must be anxious to do some more jogging.' As Romy swept her eyes over him, she noticed a smattering of grey hair at his temples. 'I know men of your age tend to be obsessed with keeping fit.' And that, she thought, puts us even after the crack about Great-aunt Prudence!

Chase's eyes darkened in fury. He guessed the girl was a good ten years younger than him, so perhaps he *did* seem old. He shifted his posture. Hell, reach your mid-thirties and you were marked down as the mature man, with senior citizenship just around the corner! He gave an inward moan of protest, but then his practical streak leapt to the fore.

'You can't wash that brush, gloss paint isn't water soluble,' he informed her pedantically. 'Clean it with turpentine or something similar.' Romy managed a nod which she hoped would indicate she had merely made a slip of the tongue, but inside her head questions began to whirr.

Where could she purchase turpentine, and how much would she need? Was there a local shop she could walk to, or did this mean another drive into San Francisco? She gave up an internal prayer—please, don't make me have to take another dose of the traffic right now. 'Are you painting with a view to the property being sold?' Chase asked, his mind equally active. Where did this girl fit into the picture? Was she some distant relation who had come out here for a holiday and was tidying the cabin on Mrs Klein's behalf? His tanned brow furrowed in question. 'Why bother? The place is an old dump and——'

'It's not for sale,' Romy intervened, and heard her stomach rumble again. After breakfasting on one slice of melon, she was hungry. Enough time had been wasted. She appreciated people taking an interest, but this Chase O'Donoghue's interest bordered on the downright nosey. What earthly difference could the cabin's future make to him?

'But it *must* be sold!' he said, through tightened jaws.

He was coming on too strong, stood there with black brows lowered and his shoulders tense, as though, in some odd way, she had spoiled his day, his week, his year! Romy had had enough. All she wanted was to grab a cup of coffee, have something to eat, and return to her labours. Lack of a radio meant lack of a weather forecast, so it made sense to accomplish as much painting as possible while the sun shone, in case the mist returned.

'On whose orders *must* it be sold?' she asked, allowing one last question.

Chase baulked at saying 'mine'. Prudence had been a mule-stubborn ornery character, could this girl be the same? He began to waffle. 'No one would want to live in this—this eyesore, and the land is so overgrown it would take years to knock it into shape.'

'The property has potential,' she declared, sticking to her guns come what may.

'As much potential as the square wheel!'

'I have plans,' Romy added mysteriously.

Chase felt beleaguered. 'Plans?'

She wafted the brush to make him back off, now desperate for her morning coffee. 'Yes, and if you would care to jog off, Mr O'Donoghue, I shall make a start at putting them in progress.'

Brush encircling her head like a Samurai's sword, Romy advanced, grinning when he retreated down the path, obviously furious, but having no option. When he was outside the gate, he halted.

'I have a proposition,' he announced, flexing his shoulders in such a way that he seemed quite capable of uprooting the gate, fence, cabin and all in one mighty heave, and tossing them into the ocean.

'Bad luck, because I'm not interested in propositions,' she told him and marched off to make coffee before he could say another word.

Chase suspected the silver-suited Miss Romy MacDonald had been having a huge joke at his expense, and he did not like it one bit. Grim-faced, he strode back up the hill, took a can of beer from the fridge and went out on to the stone-flagged patio. Below him sat the cabin, but he overlooked the rear, so there was no trace of Romy, who was doubtless busy again on the front verandah. For a few minutes he gazed down, then subsided on to a white wrought-iron chair to sip his Budweiser.

Like the whole of Chase's property, the patio was well-ordered. Trained rambler roses covered the granite boundary walls, carefully tended fuchsias bloomed in redwood barrels, and at the far end sliding glass doors gave on to the hot tub area, with its smooth gold tiles and ferny dell. During his spells abroad, a woman came in twice-weekly to water the plants and provide a little on-going cleaning, but Chase looked after the house himself when he was in residence. He could never understand why women made such a fuss about housework. It was easily done if you were methodical, a point he had often argued with Ginette.

As his thoughts returned to the tumble-down cabin, a wave of resentment swept over him. What right did some slip of a girl have to interrupt his plans—for it was only an interruption, Chase was sure. She could never have been serious about the place not being sold, could she? No, she's just playing at house, he told himself. She'll soon lose interest. But he had been banking on a straightforward transaction with Mrs Klein, and had even toyed with the idea of extending his leave should the purchase be speedily accomplished. If he made a start at dismantling the cabin before the winter set in, come spring it would be all systems go, and by next summer maybe his dream of running an underwater sports centre would have come true! But first things first. He telephoned Stu and started to explain what had happened.

'She threatened you with a paintbrush?' Stu was positively giggling. 'Hell, you're six foot two and full of muscle, can't you protect yourself? Sounds like you're lucky she didn't have rape on her mind.' He went off into guffaws of laughter which made Chase scowl.

'The point is, there seems to be a hitch,' he said, trying to bring Stu to order. 'She told me the place isn't going to be put on the market, but that has to be wrong. I want to find out what's happening.'

'Did you check out who owns the cabin now?' Stu asked, trying to adopt a businesslike tone, but with scant success.

'I didn't get the chance.'

'The paintbrush, eh?' He guffawed again. 'Well, did you get the name of the lawyers who are handling Mrs MacDonald's estate?'

'No!'

'You wouldn't like to go down there right now and ask, would you?' Chase said a few words of choice obscenity which left the other man in no doubt whatsoever of his refusal. 'How about phoning? You have Prudence's number, don't you?'

'Yes, I have, but no, I won't. If I ring, the damn girl will imagine I'm scared to face her.'

Stu was spluttering once more. 'I never thought I'd live to see the day when a woman ran rings around *you*!'

'Cut it out,' Chase retorted. 'You're my attorney, so you do the dirty work. Besides, it was the paintbrush that bugged me. She's ruined my shirt completely.'

He sounded so much like an indignant child that Stu laughed some more. 'Wait until I tell Ginette about this.'

'*Don't you dare!*'

When Stu sobered, it was decided that the best course of action would be for him to phone Romy in his role of attorney, explaining that he had an interested client and could he have an update of the situation?

'Don't give her my name, not yet,' instructed Chase, for a sixth sense warned him Stu had a better chance of success if the girl did not know the identity of the interested client. He spent a fraught half-hour pacing up and down the patio, before Stu called back to let him know a response could not be raised from the cabin. 'But the stupid broad's down there!' he exploded.

'And the line is perpetually engaged.' Stu could feel his friend's frustration zizzing along the telephone wire. 'Cool it, Chase. I'll send her a letter, she'll have it by morning.'

He ground his teeth. 'But then I'll have to wait days for a reply and I don't want to wait days. I need to know about that cabin *now*.'

'In that case, old buddie, there's no alternative but to go and see her.'

'I will!' he announced rashly, but added a characteristic note of caution. 'Send a letter with my offer, just in case.'

'In case what? In case she erects scaffolding on you and gives you a top-to-toe paint job?' Stu ended the call in gales of laughter.

Chase told himself to plan carefully. He was not about to blow another meeting with Romy by leaping in unprepared. Now, he decided, he knew what kind of character he was dealing with, and would act accordingly. As he plotted, he prepared lunch. Lunch was salad, but a serious salad, compiled with his usual expertise.

He assembled avocado, tomato, green pepper, cottage cheese, lettuce, cooked beans, alfalfa sprouts and black olives, topped off with salad dressing, blue cheese variety. Chase added two cans of beer to his tray and went on to the patio, planning his strategy as he ate. Ever practical, he decided it would be wise to wear his ruined tee-shirt and a pair of old jeans kept for gardening—that way, it would not be too disastrous if he should come into contact again with white gloss. Removing the brush from Romy's grip must be the first essential, without it she would be rendered impotent and he would feel a lot happier. Chase's confidence reasserted itself. Fairly and squarely he would state his case, keeping his somewhat erratic temper under control, because losing it would give her an edge—then he would proceed to haul her in, inch by inch. He was not unaware he possessed certain persuasive powers where females were concerned, and had no doubt matters would go his way if he bothered to lay on the charm. He had almost finished eating when he remembered he was supposed to ring Julia.

'Sorry, Chase, I'm tied up tonight. I'll have to cancel,' she told him when her secretary put him through.

'All work and no play?' he replied, the crispness of his words signifying his annoyance.

'Rubbish! It's just that I have my career to consider, like you have yours,' she shot back. 'The V.P.'s coming over from New York and we have a business meeting lined up.'

Chase shrugged. 'How about us getting together tomorrow?' Hell, they had met up once, so far,

and that had been no great shakes because Julia
had insisted on gabbling on about some plum
advertising account she had landed.

'I'll let you know in the morning,' she
promised, softening the blow with a fusilade of
kisses.

He cleared the table, washed and stacked the
pots, pulled on his old clothes and marched back
down the hill. Romy was sitting on the verandah
steps in the sunshine in her silver suit, her red
hair stuck up like a cock's comb. She was
munching sunflower seeds.

'Not you again?' she complained, as Chase
fiddled for a moment with the broken latch on
the gate. When he strode up the path she noticed
that he was different this time, friendlier, and she
held out a hand. 'Want one?' Romy was not a girl
to bear grudges, and when he accepted a
sunflower seed in the spirit it was offered, they
exchanged a smile. My word, he's *sexy*! she
thought in amazement, as he popped the seed
into his mouth and gave an experimental chew.
Thumbs tucked loosely into the pockets of his
jeans, Chase's stance was one of masculine
self-assurance, legs set apart, hips thrust slightly
forward. The fact that the jeans were a little tight
did nothing for Romy's equilibrium and her calm
began to falter. Before he had been an annoyance,
an older man, a neuter. She had not been aware
of him as an attractive male, but now she was.
Her pulse quickened. 'Like it?' she asked, trying
to ignore the bumping of her heart as he stood
over her, looking like a living advertisement for
Greek gods.

He wrinkled his nose. 'Not much.'

'What can I do for you?' she asked a little

tartly, irritated by her clichéd response to his physical attributes. 'I was told that this bay was uninhabited, apart from some monster who occasionally occupies that pile near the top of the hill, but you appear to be one of the fixtures and fittings.'

'Monster? That pile?'

The words were exhaled on a hiss. Despite his resolution to be all sweetness and light, Chase could not help glowering.

Seeing she had once again upset him, Romy theorised that he possessed a remarkably low anger threshold. Yet, under the circumstances, maybe there were advantages to having him in that state. When he had smiled she had felt a great swoop of attraction, but now that he was bad-tempered, his appeal had faded. Thank goodness! After her experience with Peter she badly needed time to take stock and had no wish to become entranced by some handsome American, though he was not strictly handsome. It was the vibrant aura he gave out of being his own man that had attracted her.

'The fellow up the hill isn't a friend of yours, is he?' she asked, and when Chase shook his head in dumb response, she continued blithely, 'I gather he took great pleasure in making my great-aunt's life pure hell. He was forever complaining about her cats and arguing. You would wonder how anyone could treat a defenceless old lady like that, wouldn't you? He sounds to be a dreadful character. The longer he stays abroad, the better. That's all I can say.' Each statement was accompanied by a swing of a tapered hand, but Chase was too incensed to notice that on this occasion she was not also swinging a paintbrush.

'You've said enough, and it's one hell of a slander!' he interjected. The green eyes looked puzzled. 'That so-called *pile* happens to be my house and *I'm* the monster!'

Romy's stomach plunged, but she smiled bravely, knowing the only way to survive was to bluff her way out. 'My information must be at fault. It was obviously some other neighbour Mrs Klein was talking about, because you seem to be—well, er—a friendly kind of person.' Inwardly she cringed. He was anything but friendly, towering over her like a human bulldozer about to trample her down. 'You and Prudence probably got on like a house on fire. I bet you kept a kindly eye out for her?'

'Don't overcompensate,' he ordered with chill violence. 'I tolerated the old gal—your great-aunt, right?' She gave a tiny bob of her head which made the red tufted hair shake. 'And she tolerated me, an arrangement which suited us both just fine.' Having set that straight, Chase moved on. 'I've come to ask who owns this property now, and what plans there are for its disposal. Many years ago a verbal agreement was made between your great-aunt's husband, Alex, and my father, that as the O'Donoghues already owned the remainder of the bay, this little patch would be offered to us when Alex kicked off. It was his belief that Prudence would move to a more civilised area if she was widowed because a lonely cabin with few amenities is no place for an old person, but unfortunately she showed an obstinate streak. She disregarded the agreement and refused to go.' He paused to check the effect of his oratory, and was relieved to see Romy looked intrigued. 'My father, Paddy, died a while back, but I consider the agreement between him and Alex MacDonald still stands. I'm entitled to buy this land, and I'll offer a reasonable price.'

He sounded so patronising that Romy wished the paintbrush was available to cut him down to size. She wafted a hand. 'Thank you, but as I happen to own the property now——'

'You!' He was appalled.

'I intend to renovate the cabin and make my home here.' She felt like adding, 'So there!' but managed to resist.

Chase scowled. 'You won't enjoy living in the bay. Life is quiet and when I'm abroad the nearest neighbour is three miles distant.' He suddenly dropped down to sit beside her on the step, and Romy saw he had decided to be persuasive. She wasn't sure if she could handle that. He was too close, the blue eyes too friendly and his grin too rakishly attractive. 'A pretty girl like you needs company, people to talk to. We get the odd hiker, but on the whole visitors are few.'

Romy popped the remaining sunflower seeds into her mouth and munched reflectively. 'There would be plenty of visitors if I opened a gift shop here.' The idea had come from nowhere, but she was pleased at having made the announcement, because Chase looked horrified.

'No way can you open a gift shop! There'd be people zooming up and down the hill, kids paddling in the bay. It would be bedlam.'

'And what were you planning to do if you had acquired my cabin, Mr O'Donoghue?' she asked with sugary politeness. 'Turn it into a retreat for geriatric joggers?'

The clench of his jaw said the jibe had hit home.

'I shall pull the cabin down, clear the land and build a diving ranch. I'm a deep-sea diver. I have the professional qualifications to give instruction, combined with a vast experience of the diving game. It can be a highly profitable career, and young men are in high demand for work on the oil rigs. I have a full training course prepared and in addition to the professional angle, I will run lessons on snorkelling and scuba diving.' He was talking as though his diving ranch was a *fait accompli*.

'But wouldn't that mean people zooming up and down the hill, too? Aren't you being a touch egocentric?' Romy accused. 'How come my ideas for development are no go, but yours are okay?' Her eyes skimmed the bay. 'There's ample room here, and as you own the majority of the land already, I'm sure it won't be too difficult to modify your plans and go ahead without swallowing up my little piece.'

Chase's mouth took on a determined slant. 'I'm not prepared to do that. Guest cottages will be sited further up the hill, but I need your land for a large swimming pool and various health-club type facilities. If you accept my offer, which is the best you'll get,' he said pointedly, 'I'll make a start this fall. The builders will move in come spring. I've already arranged for my attorney to put a letter in the post to you, outlining the price I'm prepared to pay.'

His lordly air reminded her of a medieval landowner stating terms to his serfs.

'I'm not interested in your offer,' Romy protested.

Without warning, Chase swooped from serious intent to devastating charm, producing a crooked smile which jumbled her up inside.

'You will be, when you read the details.' He spoke with one hundred per cent confidence. 'A fistful of dollars will be far more use than this old ruin. Why should you refuse?'

Romy rose to her feet. Upright she had a slight psychological advantage, and she needed every slight bit of advantage she could muster. He was too damned attractive, too persuasive. His enthusiasm for his diving ranch was intense, and for a moment she had almost felt like giving way. She swept past him up the steps to retrieve her paintbrush, another psychological aid.

'I refuse because I fully intend to make this cabin my home, and——' she continued, narrowing green eyes, 'because I have no intention of being ordered around by some acquisitive male who is interested only in himself. Don't call me, Mr O'Donoghue, I'll call you, and now—I'm busy.'

Chase looked at her for what seemed like eternity, his blue eyes hooking on to hers until she could bear it no longer, and she turned to start slapping paint willy-nilly over the wall.

'I hope I will manage to make you change your mind,' he said, and she heard him leave.

When Romy remembered his words later that day, she realised they had sounded more like a veiled threat than anything else.

CHAPTER THREE

For Romy the next few days were hectic physically, yet mentally barren. Fine weather meant she was painting from morning until night, but although her body ached from over-use when she staggered into bed, her mind was stale. She began to crave for the sound of another human voice, and when Mrs Klein's daily call did not come she was bereft, until she discovered the phone had been knocked askew and was buried beneath a pile of bed linen she had set aside to sort. Castigating herself, Romy rang the old lady, but as they had little in common they had little to say, and five minutes later she was back to feeling she was the one solitary soul on earth. The one solitary soul.

She almost wished Chase O'Donoghue would lope down like some arrogant panther spoiling for a fight, but he kept clear. When no offer appeared from his attorney, she wondered if her neighbour had changed his mind, though she would never have classed him as the type who gave in easily. More probably he was working out a different approach, and somehow her spirits were bolstered by the thought that he might appear at any moment. He didn't. Slap, slapping away with her brush on the wooden verandah, Romy had too much time to think and began chewing over the rights and wrongs of leaving London.

The so far devout conviction that she had been wise to refuse Peter's proposal began to crumble.

By anyone's standards, he was a catch. Tall, slim, blondly elegant, he was courteous to his fingertips yet, amazingly, good fun. But he had seemed too polished, too much the social animal, and after a lifetime with her father, who was the prototype of the perfect host and the entertaining guest, Romy had rebelled. She was bored with making meaningless small talk at parties, and circulating in a superficial strata of society which floated from one country to the next, armed with fixed smiles and a glass of champagne. At five years old she had started passing around the vol-au-vents, and enough was enough.

A sneaky thought surfaced. Wasn't a life on the move what she was best suited for? No, I need roots, she wailed silently. I've been shunted from pillar to post since I was in pigtails, and now I must stop. An uncanny conviction warned that if she did not call a halt she would be dragged on to a diplomatic merry-go-round and might never escape. Like her father, Peter worked for the Foreign Office. At the moment he was based in London, though he had had previous postings to India and Pakistan, postings where he had shone, wowing everyone with his flair for making friends and influencing people.

'My next secondment is Bangkok,' he had informed her. 'Thailand would be perfect for you, and you would be perfect for Thailand.'

What Peter had meant was that she would make the perfect wife for a junior diplomat who was going places in more ways than one. But a palatial rented villa held no appeal. Romy was weary of being surrounded by servants and Foreign Office furniture, weary of living her life in chunks of three years here, three years there,

of leaving behind a trail of dear friends she was
unlikely to ever meet again. She paused for a
moment's reflection, biting into her lip. From
birth she had been programmed to such an
existence, could it be this present dissatisfaction
was merely a hiccup? Maybe this idea of making a
home in California was baloney? She admitted
her track record was uninspiring. Her father's
career had had her skidding around the globe,
attending eight different schools in six different
countries, but even after leaving school she had
been restlessly mobile. Like a butterfly she had
flitted from one location to the next, discarding
this job for that—and by her own choice. Romy
wondered if she possessed the stability to find
contentment in one place. Perhaps it would take a
husband and family to steady her down . . .

After three days of tireless activity, the
verandah was completed and she wallowed in a
great surge of satisfaction, forgetting her broken
fingernails, aching limbs and painted hair. As the
front face of the little cabin shone in the
sunshine, so Romy's smile shone too, but later,
when she walked around to examine the side
walls, next on her list, the green eyes grew
pensive. Single-storey and low the building
might be, yet far more than a dining chair would
be required to gain access to the upper portion. A
ladder was vital. But acquiring one meant a
second journey into San Francisco, and she had
not yet psyched herself into braving another
skirmish from behind the steering wheel.

Romy strode up the hill, pounding on the solid
door which was set mid-centre into a high stone
wall, shielding Chase's house from the lane. She
intended to ask if she could borrow a ladder for,

of the two, her neighbour seemed slightly more approachable than the city centre. Desperately she tried to convince herself Chase had abandoned his wish to acquire her property, and with that out of the way there was really no reason why they should not get along. Okay, so he and Great-aunt Prudence had been at loggerheads, but Mrs Klein had said bluntly that her sister's behaviour would have tested the patience of a saint, and co-existing with a bunch of raggedy cats and their aroma could not have been unadulterated bliss.

When her knock received no reply, Romy pounded again. The wall looked impenetrable, and there was a Fort Knox flavour about the closed doors of the double garage further up the hill. Security appeared to be tight and when, after more poundings and a long wait, Romy heard noises on the far side of the wall, she wondered if Chase would frisk her. Bolts were wrenched aside and when the door was opened, they stared at each other in surprise. Romy's pupils dilated. With only a white towel wrapped around his waist, Chase was more a Greek god than ever. His tanned chest and shoulders were damp, and his legs bare. Wet footmarks darkened the stone flags behind him.

Romy stuck out a hand. 'I've come to ask if we can be friends,' she announced, deciding it would be wise to pave the way with gold before requesting help.

Chase looked as if he suspected her of sporting knuckle-dusters, but after a moment's hesitation he accepted her offer of friendship. His hand was big and warm and strong around hers, and his smile matched. There seemed little doubt that the virile Mr O'Donoghue could be a lady-killer if he tried, even if he hadn't had much success with Great-aunt Prudence, and the deeply tanned chest, with its coat of dark hair from throat to navel, emphasised his appeal in a way which had Romy's adrenalin pumping. She could not help imagining he would be teak-coloured from head to toe, apart from a white wedge at his hips, or maybe not even that. His patio was very private, after all ... On consideration, the city centre *would* have been less disturbing, she realised.

He grinned when he noticed her examination. 'Excuse my appearance, but you caught me in the hot tub. From nine to twelve each morning I run a sex orgy. There are six of us installed, all shapes and sizes, but we can squeeze in one more. Like to join us?'

'No!' she yelped, then her cheeks grew hot when she realised he had been kidding. Romy examined her shoes, black velvet flatties made in China.

'You prefer your sex one to one?' he drawled, and her cheeks grew even hotter. For one foolish moment she wondered if he was hinting at him and her, but then he laughed, his teeth strong and white, and she realised he was only baiting her.

'Yes, I do,' she retorted, trying to sound blasé, but when she noticed how his gaze was lingering on her breasts and hips beneath the clinging silver, she began to wish that today she had chosen to put on underwear.

'Do you generally go around dressed like a chicken in tinfoil?' he asked, leading her past flowering shrubs and around the corner of his house on to a spacious patio which overlooked the sea.

'Only in the mating season,' she quipped, and

promptly regretted the sexual content of her reply.

Romy's green eyes shot from his to scan the view beyond the low granite wall. What was happening? The more she came into contact with her neighbour, the more she was aware of him as a vibrant sensual animal. Peter had never had this effect, but she had never stood with Peter on a sunlit patio, with him wrapped in a towel and her naked beneath thin silver cloth, knowing no one else was around for miles. She and Chase could be the only people on earth, like Adam and Eve!

'Have you come to say a personal "yes" to my offer?' he asked, and for a moment Romy was too busy thinking about the two of them to work out what he meant. The balance between them had shifted. At the cabin she had been more confident, but here, on Chase's home territory, she was at a loss. He grinned, rubbing a lazy hand among the damp hairs on his chest. 'You must agree I've been generous.'

She looked at him. 'I haven't received any offer. The postman hasn't been near me.'

Puzzling over her comment, Chase locked his thumbs over the top of the towel, unconsciously sliding it lower to reveal more firm golden flesh. 'But I checked it had arrived. The mailman put the envelope into your box two days ago.'

'I have a box?' The moment the words dropped out, Romy felt stupid. There *had* to be a mail box belonging to the cabin. Didn't every home in the States have one? 'Where is it?' she asked.

'Do you mean to say I've been sitting up here in purgatory for the past few days waiting for your reply, and you've never even read the damn

thing?' he complained. 'Your box is at the top of
the lane, alongside mine. You must have noticed
them.'

'I did,' she confessed, and became a trifle
belligerent. 'How was I supposed to know one
belonged to me? They're not marked.'

'Common sense?' he enquired laconically.

Romy wished she had a paintbrush handy, for
the way Chase was dominating their dialogue
annoyed her. She much preferred to have him on
the defensive, rather than the other way around.

He bent forward to dab her cheek with a
reproving finger. 'This isn't the United Kingdom
where the letters drop on to the mat, kiddo.'

'I realise that. I'd just forgotten,' she rejoined,
stepping back from the fragment of an embrace
because it had created a minor landslide in her
shaky self-assurance.

'I'll change, then we'll go up and collect your
mail,' Chase told her. 'I'll be back in a minute.'

Before Romy could protest that she was quite
capable of seeing to her post herself, thank you,
he had disappeared, leaving her little else to do
but stand at the edge of the patio and inspect her
abode from a bird's eye stance. Chase had been
right about the roof. Originally the wooden
planking had been covered in black asphalt, but
over the years the weather had taken its toll and
now she counted too many bare patches. Come
rain, come leaks, she deduced with a sigh. She
swivelled to look at the splendid building behind
her. Everything was so spruce and well-
maintained; Chase would never allow water to
seep through *his* roof!

When he returned he looked supremely well-
maintained himself, in a crisp white shirt and

navy slacks, his dark hair brushed back, though one or two wayward curls straggled across his brow.

'Let's go,' he ordered and marched off at a rate of knots.

Romy followed. 'Do you think mending my roof would be expensive?' she asked, not bothering to stop and think that here was a man whose main aim in life was to see her roof flattened.

Chase shook his head. 'Materials wouldn't amount to much, it's a simple job. However, if you bring in workmen, the labour costs will be high.'

'You're not suggesting I repair it myself, are you?' she questioned as she tramped up the hill beside him.

'You bet I'm not.' He stopped and caught hold of her shoulders, forcing her to face him. When she looked into those blue eyes, Romy felt she had stepped into the ring with a prize fighter. 'I'm suggesting you abandon the whole foolish project and sell the property to me,' Chase said sternly. 'Soon, like yesterday. I have a moral right to that land.'

'And I have a legal right,' she shot back. Flinging wide her hands, Romy encompassed the entire bay. 'There's more than enough room here for the two of us, you're just being greedy.'

'Sorry, kiddo, you're wrong.' They had reached the T-junction with the hilltop track where two mailboxes stood in the long grass; one neatly painted, the other a rusty-hinged monstrosity. Romy knew straight away which was hers. 'Here.' Chase lifted the creaking flap, selected a foolscap envelope and placed it on top of the mail which he shovelled out into her hands. Surprised by the amount of correspondence, though most were circulars, Romy began leafing through, eager to find something from her father. Mr MacDonald had promised to telephone on her arrival, but there had been no call. Her call to London had gone unanswered, so now she hoped he had written instead, but there was no envelope covered in his flamboyant scrawl. As usual, her father had had other things to think about.

'This is the most important. Read the other mail later,' Chase ordered, wafting the topmost letter beneath her nose. 'Come back to the house and tell me what you think of my offer.'

'But I don't want to sell,' Romy protested, hurrying alongside as he held a speedy path down the hill. She was still protesting when Chase sat her down at the patio table and provided a letter opener. She gazed at the sum quoted. 'I don't have a clue whether or not this is reasonable, but in any case——'

'I'm offering a good price. Do you think I'd cheat you?'

'Well, no.' She guessed he would be fair. Keen to possess her property, Chase might be, but his dealings would be arrow straight.

'You won't get a better one,' he announced, sprawling in a chair.

'But I don't need a better offer because I'm not selling,' she wailed, refusing to be browbeaten. 'I intend to have a crack at setting up home here.'

Alert to the inference, Chase pounced. 'So living in the bay is an experiment?'

Romy motioned vaguely. 'Yes. No. I don't

know. I need time to discover if California suits me, but I'm not selling. Not yet.'

'How much time do you need?' he demanded.

'I don't know. Stop leaning on me like this,' she protested. 'Nothing is ever fixed and final. How can I tell what I'll feel like doing in the future? You're asking me to make impossible predictions.'

'You must have some idea,' he argued.

'I don't.'

'You must.'

She squirmed. Chase was applying his own version of the Chinese water torture, and something was needed to placate him. Figures were plucked from the air. 'One year or two, and if things don't work out, then I'll depart.' Romy knew she would reach a decision long before twelve months had passed by, but hoped that by quoting a grand time scale, Chase would ease up.

'Two years?' He gave a bellow of outrage. 'I can't live in limbo for two years.'

'Why not?'

'Because I'm goddamn thirty-five,' he said morosely, his anger crumpling. 'Professional diving is a young man's game, so my days for working off rigs are numbered. Soon I must opt for something less strenuous, and before I pack in diving I need to have my future arranged. That's where the ranch comes in, it's security for my old age.'

'Your old age?' It seemed incredible that the vibrant male before her could be worried about growing old, but worried he was, Romy could see it in his eyes.

'Yes,' he growled, then sat for a moment, deep in thought. 'Be sensible,' he told her, marching into battle once more. 'If you have doubts now about staying at the cabin, why spend time and money on worthless renovations?'

'I don't have doubts. Well, not many,' she adjusted, causing him to raise his eyes in frustration.

Chase slammed a clenched fist on the table, which made her jump. 'My advice to you, kiddo, is to quit. By remaining here you're just being selfish.' He was tempted to get hold of the infuriating silver siren opposite him and shake some sense into that silly head of hers.

'*I'm* being selfish, what about you?' she retorted. 'All you're concerned about is number one, but I have a future too, you know. I still maintain there's ample space here for both of us. I certainly wouldn't make a fuss about your damned diving ranch being so close at hand, so why can't you compromise and alter your plans a little?'

'Because I don't believe in compromise,' he said through clenched teeth.

'Then it's high time you changed your beliefs.' Romy pushed back her chair and swept to her feet. 'I can quite understand how you and Great-aunt Prudence came to have a vendetta, because in my opinion you are the most——' She stopped short, suddenly recalling the point of her visit. Romy hesitated, torn between a vitriolic denunciaton of his high-handed ways and needing his help. 'Do you know where I can hire a ladder?' she blurted out. She would not ask to borrow one, because that seemed too much like grovelling.

Chase looked bemused. 'What kind?'

Unaware ladders came in assorted varieties,

Romy drew an abstract version in mid-air. 'Something to enable me to paint the top of the side walls. A chair isn't high enough.'

'I have a ladder I could lend you, though I don't see why the hell I should,' he muttered. 'Give me one good reason why I should help you paint an old shack which I am to raze to the ground?'

'Because you're a good neighbour?' Romy suggested, grabbing the opportunity as a Titanic passenger might have grabbed at a lifebelt. If she could avoid taking the Buick out on the road, she would. 'And because if the cabin has a fresh coat of paint, you'll have a better view?'

Chase sighed. Maybe he would do better to humour her, and there was a mixed-up sense in what she said. 'Okay, but don't blame me if you fall off the damn thing and break your neck.'

'I won't,' she assured him, but crossed her fingers, recalling the several near misses on the chair. As Chase seemed to be in a better mood, almost generous, Romy decided she could risk asking another favour. 'Would you cut my hair for me?' She gave him a coaxing smile. 'There's paint at the ends. I've trimmed what I can off the front, but I can't see to do the back, and now it's difficult to comb.'

'You expect me to be your mailman, your equipment supplier, your hairdresser,' he grumbled. 'What do you want next—lover?' The word was a Freudian slip. Chase was as surprised as Romy when he said it, but if she insisted on going around naked beneath that shiny silver suit, a man could not be blamed for imagining what she must look like without it. 'Okay, I'll cut your hair,' he blundered, fearful of her answer. She

might say yes! He never knew quite what to
expect from the free and easy Miss MacDonald.
One minute she was berating him, the next
asking favours. 'None of that paint is wet, is it?'
he asked, frowning at the streaks of gloss which
now dappled her outfit.

'You're quite safe,' she grinned, and followed
as he led the way through sliding glass doors into
the house.

Romy was grateful he had skated over the
'lover' comment, for the word had stunned,
creating a whirl of emotions which had left her
momentarily breathless.

The lounge they had entered was luxurious,
decorated in greys and blues, though there were
contrasting touches of lime green and deep
turquoise, most vividly displayed in Thai silk
cushions which were strewn on the white leather
sofa. The pale blue Persian carpet had been
recently vacuumed, and a collection of heavy
Caithness glassware on the wall unit gleamed in
the sunshine which flooded through floor-to-
ceiling windows. A massive music centre filled
one wall, and, from the stacked precision of the
shelves, Romy hazarded a guess that the record
collection must be in alphabetical order. Chase
pushed open swing doors on to a kitchen as
sterile as an operating theatre—white tiles, yellow
polished flooring and shiny implements.

'You're very organised,' she commented,
standing back as he spread newspaper over the
floor, placed a stool on top, and found comb and
scissors.

Chase gave a small smile, which indicated he
had heard that comment before. 'My parents
were divorced when I was a kid, so my father

brought me up,' he explained. 'And anyone would be organised if they'd had Paddy around in their formative years. His creed was a place for everything, and everything in its place. I had a belt on the backside if I didn't toe the line. And I guess my career has also taught me to be orderly. You can't afford to be slipshod in deep sea diving, the risks are too great.'

'Do you dive here in California?' she asked, sitting on the stool at his direction.

Today a white satin ribbon had replaced the string, and when Romy loosened it, the thick glossy red hair tumbled around her shoulders in rippling waves. Chase was knocked askew as the flower child in the oddball outfit ceased to be, for, all of a sudden, he saw a woman, a beautiful woman.

'You look beautiful with your hair loose,' he said, before he could stop himself. An intense desire to plunge his hands into the red richness filled him. He wanted to bury his face into the softness, wrap her hair around him. Instead he folded his arms. 'You comb through and then give me instructions where to chop. About diving,' he continued, unable to tear his eyes away as she tamed the glorious mane. 'After I've been back home a week or two, the water invariably calls me. I'm not an Aquarius for nothing! The ocean's rather cold around here, so you need to be dedicated, though you're perfectly warm enough in a wetsuit. I enjoy snorkelling in the bay. There's some great underwater scenery around the rocks, and as you need a beach to get in and out of the water, everything is laid on.'

'Isn't it dangerous?'

'Not if you know what you're doing. Strictly

speaking, I shouldn't dive alone, but——' He shrugged expressively, then took over the comb. 'But I don't know what I'm doing with your hair,' he frowned. 'Why don't you dive into 'Frisco and visit a salon?'

'No, no, I don't want to do that,' Romy shuddered, visualising traffic problems. 'Besides, I may get the ends painted again.'

'You don't intend to keep chopping for ever more?' he protested. 'Can't you cover your hair?'

'How? I tried a shower cap, then a woollen beret, but I became so hot that the sweat dripped into my eyes, and I couldn't see what I was doing.' She laughed, her face alive with glee. 'I'm new to painting, and, believe me, I need all my wits about me.'

'Stand up,' Chase ordered and examined her, thoughtfully rubbing his jaw as he worked out a solution. 'Look, why not wear it this way?' he suggested, experimentally pushing his fingers into the flaming mop and twisting it behind her ears. Romy kept very still, her amusement dying beneath his touch for the strong hands sliding through her hair felt like lover's hands. Chase was so close she could feel his breath on her brow, detect the ghost of a dark beard beneath the tanned jaw, smell the clean fresh tang of soap and man. Without warning his fingers stilled and his blue eyes honed in on hers in a moment of emotional intensity which confused them both. Chase rocked forwards, his gaze sliding to her lips, such soft sweet lips. 'How old are you?' he asked, with a sharpness which sliced through the mood and set them firmly back as antagonists again.

'Twenty-two.'

She knew he had been tempted to kiss her, but had changed his mind. Romy dumped herself back down on the stool and after a moment heard the careful snip-snip of scissors at the back of her head. Chase worked with all the dedication of a doctor involved in open-heart surgery. Eventually he spoke.

'That makes me thirteen years older. I could almost be your father!'

'So what?' Romy tried to twist, but he tapped her head with the comb, warning her to keep still. She began to simmer, feeling she had been dismissed as a child, and she did not care to be dismissed, especially not by a man who, even when his black hair had turned silver, would still be devastatingly attractive. 'I think men in their thirties and forties have far more going for them then twenty-year olds,' she declared, aggrieved at having had the age gap pointed out, though she could not explain just why she should feel *so* aggrieved.

'Aw, come on,' Chase derided.

'It's true. You think of men with charisma, and they're all past thirty.'

'Like John De Lorean and Hugh Hefner?' he asked. At first she suspected he had spoken with tongue in cheek, but then he began humming as he snipped, apparently perked up by the notion that maybe there was some truth in what she had said. After making an inspection from all sides, he gave a final comb through. 'Perfect once more, ma'am.' He swooped into a low bow which had her smiling. 'Apart from a dollop of dried paint on the back of your neck.'

'Oh no!'

' 'Fraid so, kiddo, though heavens knows how

you managed that. Come on, I'll get you the ladder.'

Chase was so brisk that she knew he had rubbed out any idea of kissing her. Letters in one hand, and endeavouring to tame her hair into a ponytail with the other, Romy followed him out on to the lane. When they reached the garage, Chase pressed a switch and the double doors rolled up as if by magic.

'I didn't realise you had a car,' she commented, eyeing a polished maroon Cadillac which was parked to one side. Everything in the garage was orderly—there were tools arranged on a work bench, a section devoted to his diving cylinders, and various gardening implements suspended from racks in the roof.

'Look, we're talking America here, *everybody* has wheels,' he chided.

'Isn't there a local bus service?' she asked hopefully. 'I'd like to manage without the Buick. I can't afford to hire a car much longer.'

Chase hoisted a short aluminium ladder down from the wall, set it on to his shoulder and pressed the switch to electronically seal the garage. He set off down the hill, Romy bobbing in his wake. 'We don't have any kind of motor coach service out here. It's impossible to function without an automobile,' he said, with a look which advised she was totally off-centre.

'I could try,' she muttered, sore because he was once again voicing problems.

'Never.' When they reached the cabin, he ploughed through the long grass and set the ladder up against the side wall as she directed. 'How many coats of primer did you give the verandah?'

Dropping the letters down on the step, Romy rubbed her nose in confusion. 'I didn't.'

'Didn't use primer?' he demanded, turning to her. 'You just applied undercoat?'

'Just gloss.'

'You're nuts, you can't do that!' Chase started reprimanding her like a headmaster. 'This timber is old. It ought to be treated with primer, then undercoat, and probably at least two coats of gloss. If a job's worth doing, it's worth doing well.'

'Oh, don't be so damn pernickety,' she flung back, mad at herself for not knowing better, but equally mad at him for telling her so. 'It's *my* house, so I shall paint it as *I* like. One coat of gloss is good enough for me.' Each statement was being accompanied by sweeping hand movements.

'Romy, Romy, give yourself a break,' he sighed. 'Painting it this way is a complete waste of time. One winter, and the timber will need treating all over again.'

She clasped her arms around herself by way of protection. Romy did not want to hear his rebukes, his common sense. 'I'll take my chance,' she said tightly.

'Okay, but don't get mad at me when you realise I'm right.' Chase shrugged. 'How about climbing up the ladder to check it's high enough?'

Tentatively she mounted the rungs, growing more confident when she discovered how safe she felt. Stretching out an arm in experiment, she was grateful, nonetheless, to discover she had no need to perch right up on top. The whole upper area could be covered from a rung only three feet or so above the ground.

She grinned at him over his shoulder. 'Please can you hand me the paint and my brush? I might as well make a start right now.'

Chase pulled a face, but gingerly picked up the can she had indicated on the verandah and passed it over, taking great care to hold it at a distance. Juggling with both hands full, Romy promptly discovered that keeping your balance is not easy, even only three feet up in the air. She was attempting to lodge the can in a safe position on the topmost rung when her movements set the ladder wobbling. Her heart leapt. She was beginning to slip sideways. Seeing her plight, Chase automatically lurched into a defensive grab.

'Thanks,' she breathed, safe once more, then watched with hypnotised horror as the paint can tipped and a stream of white gloss poured in slow motion down the front of his shirt and on to his navy trousers.

Chase was livid. 'And thank you!' he snarled in tight-lipped fury, looking down as the white liquid drip-dripped, some even reaching his shoes. With the predatory swoop of a wild animal, he grabbed Romy off the ladder and into his arms. 'Now see how *you* like being covered in paint,' he roared, twisting her around and rubbing himself against her until the front of her harem suit was slippery with white gloss. Carried away by his need for retaliation, Chase was breathing hard, his eyes glittering, but without warning, the perspective changed. In addition to being furious, Romy realised he was aroused, and the hard rub of his body through the cloth of her suit began to arouse her, too. 'You dumb broad, you're the square root of useless,' he growled and kissed her savagely.

As his mouth covered hers, Romy's head swam. He needed and created a response in a single moment, and the paint between them was forgotten. A powerhouse of screwed-up emotions had been released. Chase's mouth was hot and hard, for the kiss combined punishment with desire. He wanted to hurt her, but he also found her sexually stimulating, maddening as that might be. Hands gripping her back, he locked her to him, the paint fusing them together, a sticky, semi-fluid gel which heightened the impact of one throbbing body against another. As Romy's lips were forced apart, her arms moved upwards intent on coiling around his neck, but Chase tensed. He ripped himself free, and there was an almost comical slurp as the paint bond broke.

'Enough!' He was aloof, stony-eyed as though the kiss had never happened. 'Haven't you done enough damage without putting paint in my hair as well?'

'I wasn't——' she began, bewildered by his attack, but when Romy looked down at her fingers, she saw they, too, were wet with paint. If she had been allowed to wrap her arms around his neck, she would have left behind ten sticky imprints.

'Hell, I should have learned by now that I tangle with you at my peril,' he stormed, chest heaving. 'First you try to kill me with that damned car and now, and now——' Words failed him. Perhaps it was just as well.

'Would it help if I offered to pay for new clothes?' Romy inserted timidly.

He swung a sinewed sword arm. 'No, it would not. This is the end. The *end*! From now on, you keep out of my life and I'll keep out of yours. I've had it with you, up to here.' Chase sliced a theatrical hand across his throat. 'I imagined Prudence and her cats were the pits but, kiddo, in comparison to you they were fairies on a Christmas tree!'

CHAPTER FOUR

'HE said that!' Romy's father chuckled, enjoying the joke from thousands of miles away. 'The entire episode sounds like a slapstick movie to me.'

'And to me, *now*,' she agreed. 'You should have seen him stomping back up the hill with his arms held out from his body like a furious sumo wrestler. Mind you, it didn't seem so funny at the time. And the paint got everywhere! I scrubbed and scrubbed, but gloss was ingrained in my skin and down the sides of my fingernails. I used up a whole tin of scouring powder, but still I was tacky. I've been wearing that silver harem suit.' She paused, wondering if her father might be offended to hear of its bizarre role, but when there was no comment she realised he had probably forgotten he was the benefactor. 'So that's all mottled. I dried the suit off in the sun, and now I leave behind a trail of white flakes when I walk.'

'But you're quite well, apart from your mishaps with this Molotov cocktail of a neighbour?'

After no contact whatsoever, Mr MacDonald had telephoned out of the blue and was eager to catch up on her news. The comic always delighted him, and judging from his amusement at the spilled paint story, Romy had a shrewd suspicion he would soon be recounting a polished version at the dinner parties he frequented!

73

'I'm fine, though driving on the wrong side of the road still flusters me.' She told him about her experiences in the Buick, but did not reveal that what flustered her most was Chase. 'So I was forced to drive into the town centre and buy turps,' she finished up. 'But at least on that visit I didn't get lost.'

'San Francisco is a beautiful city.'

'I agree.'

Her second excursion had proved to be far less traumatic than the first, even if she had left white smudges on the steering wheel. On this occasion, Romy had been calm enough to appreciate her surroundings. She had loved the houses which clung so precariously to the hills; three-storey houses, ranging from the pretty to the grotesque, painted in sugar-almond colours of pale apricot, pistachio and soft pink. The bay, with the distant prison island of Alcatraz, was a fascinating area, and she had promised that once the cabin was properly organised, she would explore.

'So what stage are you at now, renovating Prudence's free gift?' her father asked.

'Still painting.' Reluctantly accepting the wisdom of Chase's advice, Romy had spoken to the man in the do-it-yourself store about how to treat ancient timber. 'I'm finishing off the second of the side walls. I have to apply two coats of primer, then undercoat and, finally, gloss, so it takes ages. Fortunately the weather is great, so I'm able to work nonstop.'

'No time off for good behaviour?'

'None. Have you seen anything of Peter?'

The young diplomat had sent one brief note, written when he was on the brink of rushing out to some reception or other, but Romy had been unable to determine from its tone whether or not he bore any grudge. She was worried in case Peter had not taken her refusal seriously. Maybe, like her father, he viewed her present antics as a girlish sortie. Maybe he expected her to return home in due course, with her tail between her legs, ready to fall in with his plans. Well, he's wasting his time, she thought defiantly.

'Peter's fine. He sends his love,' her father said carelessly. 'By the way, I'm off to the Far East in a week or two. There's a crisis in one of the Consulates and I've volunteered to check things out.'

'Pa! You never keep still longer than it takes to sneeze,' she protested, listening with resignation as he enthused about his anticipated travels.

'I'll ring again before I depart,' he promised.

'You do that,' she rejoined, knowing he could well find himself in some steamy tropical clime. before he next remembered his only daughter.

Romy returned to her painting, but the effervescence of her father's call seemed to have knocked her adrift and she spent most of the day trying to adapt to being alone once more. The occasional hiker crossed a distant hillside, and she heard a few cars on the track high above her, but Romy felt too aware of the silence. Maybe she should buy a radio next time she was in San Francisco? Even a disembodied voice would be company.

Knowing Chase was somewhere around, albeit incommunicado, was a comfort. True to his word, he had kept well away, though she saw him setting off on his jog each morning, a commitment which appeared to verge on the religious.

One evening a sleek sedan arrived to park

outside his garage, and Romy felt curiously peeved when a leggy blonde unfolded herself from its depths. Trim in a white suit, the girl was a perfect match for Chase, who came out to greet her looking debonair in ice-blue shirt and slacks. 'The beautiful people,' Romy had grumbled to her paintbrush, making sure she kept out of sight. In the flaking silver suit, with her hair twisted into a bun and covered by a protective triangle of polythene, she was at the opposite end of the sartorial scale. Romy had not realised Chase O'Donoghue had a girlfriend and, next morning when the sedan left, she adjusted 'girlfriend' to 'lover'. It was only natural he would have a lover, she told herself, refusing to admit that she cared. Chase was too male and healthy and attractive to be celibate. Probably he had girls lined up all over the world.

Romy was grateful the blonde's visit proved to be a one-off, and that the coast was clear when she was ready to start painting the cabin's rear wall. Chase already thought she was crazy, but she did not relish having a well-tailored young woman looking down at her in her odd outfit, and laughing. She did have some pride!

The rear wall was the last lap, but though she started off with gusto, the final brush-stroke, so long awaited, was an anti-climax. Gleaming white in the sunshine, Romy knew the cabin far outshone the splendour of the Taj Mahal, but needed to share her delight. Completing the back-breaking task should have been a time for rejoicing, for pats on the back, but instead Romy collected up the empty can, dumped the brush into a jar of turpentine, and nearly burst into tears. Where was the elation? Next on the agenda came the fence, and after that she intended to have a bash at papering the living-room, for now her enthusiasm had nosedived to zero. Romy sniffed hard. Tomorrow I'll take a holiday, she decided. I need some joy in my life.

Her first joy was not having to leap up at the blare of the early morning alarm. She lay abed until after nine, then ate a leisurely breakfast. Not having to climb into the confines of her harem suit was the second joy. Instead Romy pulled on brief white satin shorts and a matching boob tube, and revelled in the freedom. She swung her hips and chorused out a pop song as she made the bed, and then stood on the verandah, gulping in deep breaths of sea air. For almost three weeks the bay had been a backdrop to her activities, but she had not set foot on the sand, nor ventured right nor left. Today all that was destined to be changed.

Despite the sun's warmth, there was a crispness to the morning, so she tugged on a white satin jerkin and set off at a brisk jog towards the far rocks. Sea breezes sifted through her hair, left loose around her shoulders for once, and she felt uninhibited and lighthearted, like a child let out of school. For much too long she had been an automaton on a ladder and now she indulged in an energetic keep-fit session, touching her toes and doing jumping jacks. Once she kicked so exuberantly that her flip-flop sandal shot high into the air and she went in search, giggling at her own foolishness. The exercises were abandoned when she discovered shells among the sand, and by the time she gained the rocks her pockets were heavy with a bounty of shells and smooth stones.

Happily she noseyed around, peering into pools left by the tide and smiling at shoals of tiny fishes which darted beneath the curl of the waves. Around the rocks the water was deep but clear, its swell lifting long yellowy-brown strips of seaweed into a slow swirling dance. Once Romy skidded on the rubber soles of her flip-flops and nearly came a cropper, so she was grateful when she found a wide flat stone and could plonk herself down in safety to watch the oceán.

A peculiar whooshing sound made her frown, until she discovered a snorkel tube was being cleared, the water spraying into the air. Gliding towards her through the water was a lean figure in a black wetsuit, hips moving in a leisurely crawl action. It had to be Chase, propelling himself so professionally, arms by his sides. He was relaxed. Romy wished she was. She had been, until she had noticed him, but now her insides twisted into a knot. How would he greet her? Was he still furious about the ruined shirt and trousers? Her green eyes were wide and wary as he surfaced. For a moment he trod water, pushing the mask up on to the top of his head and removing the metal tube from his mouth.

'Hi, there,' he said and grinned, untroubled by the seawater coursing down his tanned face. 'How do you fancy going out to dinner tonight?' Romy could not have been more surprised if he had slapped her across the face with a wet fish. 'Stu and Ginette Beazley, some friends of mine, have invited me to eat at their place and I wondered if you'd care to come along?'

'Beazley?' A bell rang in her mind.

'Stu's my attorney, we go back years.' Romy

nodded, recalling that his offer for the cabin had originated in the office of Stuart M. Beazley. 'Ginette's an acquired taste, but Stu is a regular guy,' he continued, appearing to be as at home in the water as he was on dry land.

Romy did not know what to say. An evening in civilisation was tempting, but was he merely bringing in reinforcements? Maybe he intended for his attorney to also have a shot at brainwashing her into selling the cabin? Chase *had* to have an ulterior motive. Grief, he had ignored her for days, so what made her so fascinating now? Never one to prevaricate, Romy said what was on her mind.

'Why invite me? Why don't you ask one of your—your friends, like that blonde girl who visited you last week?' She didn't add, 'the one who stayed all night'. She didn't have to, it was there in her tone and Chase picked up all the implications.

'Julia? That was a passing attraction which has passed. I just thought you would enjoy an evening out. It would make a change.'

'Ye-es.'

Playfully he flicked water on to her rock, splashing her toes before she had a chance to pull back.

'Up until now I'd half suspected you had balloon shaped legs to match your balloon shaped pants, seems I was wrong,' he grinned. 'You sure look different now that you've stopped slapping on paint. Real gorgeous.'

She replied with a cautious smile. He was out to charm, but even armed with that knowledge Romy found it difficult to ignore his crooked grin, the friendly blue eyes.

'Thanks for the loan of the ladder,' she said primly. 'I've finished all the high work now.'

'Fine, but hang on for a while. You might need it later.' Chase gestured towards the beach. 'Why don't you retrace your steps and wait for me, then I can fill you in about this evening?'

Romy agreed, and watched as he replaced his mask and turned to swim away. Why not accept the invitation? She was lonely, bored with her own company and, if she was honest, would much prefer to have Chase as a friend. What was the sense in them being the only people in the bay, yet at daggers drawn? Intent on returning to the beach, she pushed herself upright and swivelled, but unexpectedly her foot shot off at an awkward angle. With a squeak of dismay, she performed an impromptu splits, her legs stretched painfully wide, and toppled sideways into the icy depths of the Pacific Ocean. Water flooded her mouth, her throat, her eyes. Thrashing around for dear life, Romy spluttered as a wave broke over her head, bouncing her against the rocks.

'Help!' she babbled, choking on salt water.

She was out of her depth, but she could swim, and common sense rapidly reasserted itself. She managed to get her bearings and grab on to a rock, gasping for breath. Chase was yards away, his back to her, the wide shoulders flexed as he prepared to dive below the surface, but before he did, he happened to glance around. His eyes widened behind the mask when he caught sight of her bobbing in the water, her long red hair plastered across her face.

'What the hell?' He turned, but when he realised she was shocked rather than hurt, his mouth began to curve. With slow arrogant grace he swam back to her, the mask pushed on to the top of his head. 'You should have told me you fancied a dip,' he said, laughing.

Romy doggy paddled. There was no room for much more because they were trapped in a rocky lagoon, with only a narrow exit to the sea. She hated his dancing eyes, the typically masculine way he was trampling over her feelings. Did he have no pity? The water was freezing, her lovely satin jerkin and shorts had been spoiled, she had scraped a leg on the rocks, but what mattered most was that her pride was hurt.

'This is your fault!' she accused, teeth chattering as she looped a seaweedy strand of red hair behind one car.

'*My* fault?'

She found no difficulty in blaming him. 'You made the rock wet by splashing me. That's why I slipped.'

'Nonsense! You should know better than to go climbing around rocks in rubber thongs,' Chase replied, trying to find a straight face in his repertoire of expressions.

Romy stared down at the legs and feet which were paper-white in the icy water. 'My flip-flops, I've lost them,' she wailed.

Chase dived, surfacing seconds later, Neptune-like, the rubber sandals dangling from one finger. 'Yours, I believe, ma'am?' he smiled, acting as though he was a cavalier returning a lace handkerchief, but when he abruptly became alert to her shivers, he parked the footwear and snorkelling gear on a rock and glided closer. 'The swimming lesson is over,' he announced, spreading his hands to encircle her waist. 'Come on, kiddo, time to get out.' If there had been any alternative to Chase manhandling her, Romy would have taken the greatest pleasure in rejecting his help, but one look at the ledge above her head told her she would never manage to climb out on her own. He hoisted her against him, telling her to put her arms around his neck, and then rounded his hands on her hips as he heaved her out of the water. 'Hell, you must weigh a ton!' he complained, depositing her on the rocks where she panted like a bedraggled mermaid, the tangled red hair dripping down her back. He eyed her bulging pockets. 'What have you got there?'

'Stones and shells,' she replied, pushing out a mutinous lower lip.

'No wonder you were so heavy. You're damn lucky you didn't sink straight down. Just tell me, why, in hell's name, you choose to walk around weighed down with stones?'

'I like them.'

Chase shook his head, once again letting her know he considered she was an oddball, then he became practical. 'I'll take your sandals to the beach, and you make your way barefoot over the rocks,' he instructed. 'Take it slowly, it'll be painful, but it's the safest way. And I'd empty my pockets, if I were you.'

Her composure shot to pieces, Romy did as she was told. Discarding her treasure-trove, she tiptoed carefully over the crags, wincing and muttering, all the while conscious of Chase watching her progress from the sea. There was something in his take-charge manner which both inspired confidence and yet infuriated her. With a sigh she regained the sand, and plodded to meet him. The September breeze had become an

Arctic gale, whipping the wet jerkin against her, bringing gooseflesh to her shivering limbs and she was pale-faced when Chase emerged from the water. He straddled the waves, moving easily in the figure-fitting shiny black rubber wetsuit. He came to a halt before her, and stood first on one leg and then on the other, as he removed the fins from his feet.

'Get that circulation going,' he ordered. 'And I don't need to pay a penny for your thoughts. You're thinking that the old bastard is at it again—telling me what to do.'

'Right first time,' Romy said flatly.

'But I *am* right.' Chase was not worried one iota by her opinion of him. 'This breeze is making your anorak colder by the minute. Give it to me and then leap around. Hurry up.'

With numb fingers she fumbled at the zip, but could not make it move. 'I can't,' she bleated.

He gave a mock growl of exasperation and stepped forward to do the job for her. Hands by her sides, Romy stood like a subdued child as he slid open the fastening and helped her out.

'Run on the spot,' he said, slinging the jerkin over his shoulder.

Feeling somewhat foolish, she ran on the spot, but as she grew warmer, she had to admit to a sneaking admiration. Chase always seemed to know exactly what to do. She had branched out into an activity of her own, swinging her arms above her head, when she noticed the way his eyes were lingering on the bob of her breasts beneath the skimpy boob-tube. In calm control he might be, but every cell in his body was masculine, and the caress of those eyes made her all too conscious of the way she must look, breasts firmed by the chill, wind, hips moulded with creased wet satin. She stopped dead.

'I'm warm now,' she assured him. 'I'll run back home and change.'

Chase had not yet finished his penetrating appraisal. 'You've grazed your leg. Do you have some cream?'

Romy glanced down to see that her thigh had been scraped raw where she had bounced against the rocks. 'It's not bleeding much, I'm okay.'

She turned landwards, but he caught hold of her arm, drawing his hand slowly down until his fingers were interlaced with hers. Whether it was the cold or the shock, Romy did not know, but she could not find the will to pull free. The feel of his hand around hers was intensely comforting.

'No, kiddo, it's not okay,' he insisted gently. 'I'll go up home and have a look in my medicine chest for something soothing, and you have a hot shower. Put on warm clothes and then make yourself a cup of hot coffee. Make two,' he amended. 'I'll join you.'

Despite a feeling that she had been reined in and set on to the course Chase preferred, regardless of her own wishes, Romy did his bidding and twenty minutes later she had revived. Snugly dressed in her pink jumpsuit, her hair towel-dried and left to curl loosely around her shoulders, she was carrying out a tray of coffee and cookies on to the verandah when he arrived back. His black rubber wetsuit had been swapped for a red and white checked shirt and denims.

'How do you feel now?' he enquired, taking a mug of coffee as he sat down beside her on the steps. 'I know it's none of my business, but I'd suggest you get more suitably dressed the next time you go swimming.'

'I'm fine, thank you,' she said, choosing to ignore his amusement.

His concern was genuine, but Romy did not trust the devilish little flame which danced in his blue eyes. She suspected her plunge into the ocean was no more than he expected from a harum-scarum redhead, who ran around in a silver suit, but she was not sure she was satisfied with the image she seemed destined to project.

He took a small tube from his shirt pocket. 'Here's the cream. Would you like me to massage it into your thigh for you?' he asked with a grin.

'I can manage,' she assured him and scampered back indoors, pulse racing, to apply the cream herself. The crooked grin was still there to unsettle her when she returned.

'Shame that satin outfit of yours had to get a dunking, but I bet you brightened up their day for a helluva lot of fishes.'

'About this invitation to dinner,' Romy began, wanting to bring an end to his teasing. No doubt about it, she had been on her own far too much if a casual bantering from Chase had her heart thumping like a jungle tom-tom.

'Stu and Ginette have a house in a dormitory community not too far from here,' he explained, and proceeded to give a thumbnail sketch of the location. With Chase matter of fact, Romy was able to regain her poise, though her apparent inability to cope with him when he lapsed into the joky and semi-sensual dismayed her. She knew he was only indulging in lighthearted fun and wondered why she found it so difficult to respond in kind. In the past she had had her fair share of admirers and had skilfully played the flirting game, so why did Chase have her blood running like quicksilver? 'I understand another couple will be going along,' he said. 'I haven't met them, but I guess the woman will be one of Ginette's soulmates. They've probably learned how to make a meaningful casserole together.'

'What's a meaningful casserole?'

Chase was dry. 'According to Ginette nothing ever happens by chance, every action is bestowed with layers of significance. Add a shake of paprika to a casserole and she reckons you're hot-tempered or passionate, or you'd like to be—that kind of angle. The fact you could simply enjoy the taste of paprika, or think that it adds a little colour, counts for nothing. For years she's attended group therapy, so she's always shooting off her mouth about self-awareness, and ids and egos. She's obsessed with psychic activity. Added to all this, she sees herself as a do-it-yourself analyst. I've told her she's wasting the free consultations she insists on giving to friends——'

'You?' Romy interrupted.

'Yeah, me!' he drawled. 'I've said I'll finance her in a fancy office with black velvet walls and a kinky couch.' The blue eyes were dancing again. 'She could analyse you at the drop of a hat, you being accident prone and——'

'I am not! My life was a bed of roses until I met you. You're some kind of jinx.' Romy circled her mug in the air. 'And I'd like to point out that *you're* the one who nearly wrote off my car and that the paint spilled on *you*.' Conveniently she did not mention her recent dip in the sea.

Chase caught hold of her windmilling arm, and

landed it safely. 'That, kiddo, is a moot point. And don't you dare spill coffee on me.'

They exchanged a look which began to develop into a mutual grin, and suddenly the tension broke and they were laughing. Romy drained her mug and pushed it aside.

'I apologise for the arm waving. Once I had a Spanish nanny who semaphored constantly and my father reckons I picked up the habit from her. He blames all my faults on the nannies. When we lived in Hong Kong I developed a particularly disgusting sniff, identical to that belonging to the Chinese amah!'

'So I should thank heavens you didn't have a nursemaid who was a cannibal, otherwise I'd have pieces missing?' Chase paraded a tanned forearm, so Romy opened wide her mouth and pretended to take a bite. 'How come you're so well travelled?' he asked.

'My father is a diplomat.'

'Where else have you lived?' She reeled off a list of countries parrot-fashion. 'And why come to California?'

Noticing his hint of reproof, Romy felt disgruntled. Chase might be acting the friendly neighbour right now, but she would be wise to keep in mind that underlining all his actions was the unswerving desire to take control of the cabin and send her on her way.

'I came because Great-aunt Prudence bequeathed me this property in her will.'

'Why did she leave it to you?' he asked.

'I don't know. We'd never met, so I can only presume that because she and Mrs Klein were at odds, mine was the name she pulled out of the hat. Her husband was my father's uncle, but even their connection was slight.'

'Alex was a nice old guy.' Chase frowned at the glare coming off the sea. 'With a history like yours, I doubt you'll stick in here for long. You're bound to be restless.' He was rebuffing her again.

'I am not! Well——' Vague doubts made her stop and start again. 'Most of my life I've lived in rented accommodation, and I've always wanted a base, someplace which belongs to me. And now I have the cabin. It was written in the stars that I should come here.'

'The stars?' He did not sound impressed.

'Yes. I like the bay, and as soon as I have the cabin overhauled I shall find myself a job, and——'

He did not allow her to go further. 'You told me you were planning to open a gift shop!'

'I've changed my mind.'

'There you are—you're capricious!' Chase announced, his smug smile indicating she had proved his theory.

Romy kept her tone level. 'That was just a whim. A gift shop would be no use down here, there's no passing trade.' She grinned at her understatement.

'At last you're talking sense! Sausalito would make a far better location.'

'Where's Sausalito?'

Chase looked at her as if she was asking the whereabouts of New York. 'I don't get it,' he said, raking a hand though his hair. 'How come you don't know about Sausalito?'

Romy's full mouth thinned. Did he have to perpetually set her in the role of airy-fairy eccentric? 'Think of it this way,' she said tightly.

'I've been working on the cabin day-in, day-out for what seems like forever, so apart from two brief excursions into San Francisco, I've stayed put.'

She suddenly realised that Chase had made no comment about the freshly finished white walls. Well, if he chose to ignore her handiwork, that was up to him. She most certainly would not grovel by bringing it to his attention.

'Sausalito is a fishing village at the northern end of the Golden Gate Bridge,' he explained. 'It's a regular stop on all the sight-seeing tours because of the quaint harbour, and the shops and restaurants. You should pay a visit, just in case you don't get to be here too long,' he added sneakily. 'But carry a sweater when you move around this part of California, because the micro-climates can catch you on the hop.' Romy raised her brows in question. 'On a summer afternoon you can be roasting at over a hundred degrees, but travel ten miles and suddenly the temperature drops below sixty,' he explained. 'For example, you'll find it far warmer at Stu's than here.' Casually he slid his fingers beneath the heavy fall of hair and began to massage her neck. 'Will you come to dinner with me? I'd like it very much if you would.'

At his touch, Romy's composure shattered. One minute she felt like hitting him, the next she wanted to press her cheek against his chest. Grief, Chase O'Donoghue was a frustrating individual!

'Yes, I'll be pleased to come.'

'Thanks.' He sounded truely grateful, but a moment later he jumped to his feet and became businesslike. 'What's next for renovation?' he asked, looking round.

Surely now Chase must praise her on the gleaming state of the cabin walls? She waited for a compliment, but was disappointed. 'The fence,' she said sharply.

He strode off down the path to test one of the uprights. 'You'll renew?'

No, I don't have sufficient funds. Repainting is the best I can manage.' Romy joined him to gaze down at the shaky structure, then flashed him an impudent look. 'Using primer and undercoat before gloss, as instructed. Sir! But first I must clear away some of this undergrowth.' She poked a toe at the weeds growing between the wooden posts.

Shrewdly, Chase assessed what was involved. The front garden was small, but a vast rectangular unkempt plot stretched off to one side of the cabin, bounded by broken-down fencing. 'I could help,' he offered.

Romy was thrust on to the alert. 'You? Why?'

He shrugged. 'The land needs to be cleared before I can make any headway with my diving ranch.'

So everything revolved around his *own* plans! She folded her arms and started to glower, then brought herself up short. Clearing the garden was a major hurdle and what did his motives matter? If Chase was prepared to hack down thickets and bushes in the ill-conceived belief he was furthering his own ends, wasn't that his funeral?

'You're on,' she sparked.

He matched her jaunty air. 'There's no need for wages, a kiss at the end of each day will suit me fine. Double on Sundays.'

'You should be so lucky.'

He was ready to start. 'Can you rustle up

hammer and nails? We'll tackle this methodically. After the weeds around the fence have been cleared, I'll check out all the staves. There's no point starting to paint until the fence is something like sturdy.'

Romy was not sure whether she was annoyed or grateful that he was taking charge, once again. There was a temptation to ask facetiously if the fence was to be an integral part of his beloved diving centre, but she recognised Chase was prepared to fix it as a reward for giving him permission to clear the land.

Encased in her silver suit, she worked beside him for the rest of the morning. Her freedom had been shortlived, and there was a feeling of having been buckled back into a strait-jacket, but at least she did not worry if the shabby cloth-of-silver was torn on the undergrowth. When the worst of the weeds had been cleared from the base of the fence, Romy steadied the slats while Chase nailed them back into position, or refixed loose ones into the ground. Secretly she admitted that she far preferred to work in tandem, and as long as they avoided the future which they were both striving for at cross-purposes, the conversation was easy.

'Would you like some lunch?' she enquired, when Chase wiped the sweat from his glistening brow and stepped back to take stock. For the first time the fence actually looked respectable, and she could imagine how fine it would be, emblazoned with paint.

'Not sunflower seeds or macrobiotic stuff?' he checked. 'Me no like.'

'You're an opinionated so-and-so!' she told him.

'Aren't I?' he agreed unrepentant.

Romy mentally assessed her larder. 'There's fresh fruit, a tin of ravioli, and some nori. Maxim's it's not,' she apologised.

'Nori, what the hell's that?'

'Strips of dried Japanese seaweed.'

Chase clutched at his stomach. 'You come to me,' he said quickly.

'Don't you prepare proper meals for yourself?' he asked quarter of an hour later as they sat on his patio tucking into one of his salad specials, which incorporated fresh shrimps, mashed avocado, bacon strips and peach halves.

'Not too often,' Romy confessed. 'Since I've been here I've had a tendency to grab whatever's edible and carry on working.'

'You need good food, otherwise you'll be wasting away,' he rebuked, then laughed. 'Though when I think back to you in that satin outfit maybe I'm kidding myself.'

She was grateful that the telephone rang at that point and Chase removed himself, and his laughing eyes.

'Ginette, checking her guest list,' he explained on his return. 'Dinner is set for nine, so I'll come down around eight.' He looked at her, hands on hips, his dark head tilted. 'Do you have a kilt?'

Romy laughed in surprise. 'No, I don't. Why?'

'Ginette was bugging me,' he explained, with an embarrassed grin. 'She's so damned nosy about my—my friendships, and when she began to put me through the seventh degree I played up the novelty value of you being a Scot. I guess I could have overdone it.'

'So the Beazleys are expecting some girl who'll

say "Och, the noo" and do the Highland fling at regular intervals?'

'Something like that,' he agreed, sitting down opposite her.

'Bad luck. As you pointed out before, I don't even have a Scottish accent.'

His mouth crooked. 'Well, at least you're called MacDonald and you have red hair. Maybe if you drink Scotch all night, that'll convince them? Whereabouts do you come from in Scotland?'

'I don't. I don't come from anywhere, that's the problem. My father's a Scot, but my mother was English, and I was born in Australia. Pa's content to be classed as a citizen of the world, but that's always been too vague for me. I need to belong—somewhere. Maybe California?' she suggested, and was hurt when he shook his head.

'You say your mother *was*?' he questioned.

'She died when I was a baby.'

'And doesn't your father worry about you living here alone?' Chase sounded as if *he* would worry if he was in her father's shoes.

'Pa's vague about family ties. He loves me,' she added hastily, seeing him frown. 'But he prefers to skim around without the hindrance of personal relationships, and imagines everyone likes to do the same. Being in the diplomatic whirl, he seems to have all the feedback he needs from his social life. If he doesn't attend six or seven functions a week, he thinks the world is coming to an end!'

'So why do you call yourself a Scot?' Chase asked, picking up the original point.

'I am *half* Scots,' she said. 'But the real reason is a piece of whimsy, I suppose. I used to spend summers with my cousins at their home on the banks of Loch Lomond,' she explained. 'I loved

those holidays so much that for a long time I used
to pretend it was *my* home, too.'

'Wishful thinking?'

'Yes,' she agreed. 'My father has a service flat
in London, but it's a soulless place. The house on
Loch Lomondside was a real home, full of life.
Kids and dogs rushing around, muddy welling-
tons on the mat, mouthwatering smells of home
baking, my uncle mowing the lawn, church on
Sundays. It was so solid, so permanent, and I was
so envious! I would have traded in all the exotic
places I'd seen, like a shot.'

'So a few summers is virtually your only
connection with Scotland?' Chase said wryly. 'I
guess on those terms I'm more Scottish than you
are. I had a five-year stretch working on the oil
rigs off Aberdeen.'

They talked on, and Romy realised, from the
variety of diving jobs he had undertaken, that
Chase was no slouch as an international traveller
himself.

'But you always come back home to the bay
when you have leave?' she asked. 'There's never
the temptation to shoot off to the bright lights or
palm beaches?'

'Never.' His gaze slid to the grassy meadows
rolling down to the sea. 'This land is part of me,
and I'm a part of this land.'

Romy felt awful. He had not said that she was
meddling in his love for his own small part of
California, but she detected the unspoken
inference. This is emotional blackmail, she
thought, whether intentional or not. He'll be
bringing on the violins next, and telling the sob
story of how a hard-hearted Hannah is trying to
rob him of his birthright. But *her* yearning for a

home counted—didn't she have an equal need?
And wasn't Chase's overwhelming desire to
control the entire bay just a male ego trip?

Romy was still trying to sort out her muddled
thoughts when they returned to work.

'You start priming the fence, and I'll begin on
clearing the yard,' he told her, raising his brows
at the luxuriant growth. 'Though I reckon native
bearers and a machete are needed if I'm to slash
my way through that lot!'

Time flew. Mid-afternoon, Chase went up to
his house to fetch cans of beer, and by the time
the sun had become an orange ball in the sky, the
fence was half primed and the beginnings of a
bonfire now sat in the centre of the plot. Romy
moaned as she straightened, a hand to her aching
back. She pressed the lid on to the can, and
grimaced at her fingers, smeary with primer.

'Think you can work a transformation in the
next hour, kiddo?' Chase grinned, eyeing her
bedraggled silver suit.

She pushed back the red hair from her eyes. 'I
need a Fairy Godmother, and a doctor with a
syringe of painkiller. I swear my spine is locked
into a permanent S-bend.'

As he passed by, Chase patted her bottom.
'You're getting old,' he told her, and strode away
up the hill, leaving her in no doubt that he had
enjoyed sharing her labours. But only because he
imagines he is one step further towards his
damned diving ranch, she reminded herself
bitterly.

The manmade orderliness of the commuter
suburb came as a shock to the system. Although
only a matter of days since Romy had been in San

Francisco, among buildings and people, it felt like years. She smoothed fingers, now free of primer, over a hip moulded into tight cream suede pants and satisfied herself that although she felt like a country cousin, she did not look like one! Teamed with the suede pants she wore a mocha-shaded classical silk shirt, and had fastened a plethora of slender gold chains around her neck. A wide gold belt emphasised the narrowness of her waist, and Romy wiggled her toes in golden sandals, thinking how high and feminine they felt in comparison with the work-a-day flatties. Her red hair had been freshly-shampooed, blow-dried into a soft curling style around her face, and for the first time in days her face was painted. Jade eyeshadow echoed the astonishing colour of her eyes, and her lips were moist with a rosy gloss. As a final touch she had sprayed 'Opium' behind her ears and at pulse points.

When she had opened the front door in response to Chase's knock, he had looked at her, appearing momentarily stunned by the switch from oddball to glamour puss. Romy had thought she sensed a new feeling between them, something fleeting and uncaptured, something Chase would never acknowledge, but which existed nonetheless.

'Managed to get your hands clean, kiddo? I don't want you messing up my car,' he had joked, making her wonder if she had been mistaken.

She knew that, in the main, he considered she was a mixed-up kid, yet he was not entirely immune to her appeal as a woman. He had wanted her when he kissed her, and hadn't he told her she was pretty, and that he liked her figure and her hair? He had, but that didn't stop him from treating her as though she was a member of the D-stream. She wondered if he had told the Beazleys about her escapades—the spilled paint and all. As they drove through the tree-lined streets, making small talk, Romy began to feel uneasy. She had no wish to be viewed as a kooky acquaintance who happened to be Scottish into the bargain. If she wasn't a true Scot, neither was she a true kook!

Dangerously her thoughts turned to imagining how it would feel if everyone believed she was Chase's girlfriend, even his lover? The idea was fascinating—as a piece of makebelieve—but when Romy discovered that 'lover' was exactly the role Chase had preordained she should play, she was furious!

CHAPTER FIVE

Stu and Ginette Beazley were a friendly couple who welcomed her into their home with open arms, and with more than a little curiosity. Stu, a cheerful thick-set man in a floral Hawaiian shirt, whom Romy liked on sight, nodded approval as though she met some mysterious criteria, and his wife surprised her by hugging her close and whispering, 'Congratulations, honey,' into her ear. Romy gave a bewildered smile, but there was no chance to discover the reason behind those congratulations, because she was being whisked into a comfortable oak-panelled living-room where a second couple waited. Stu made the introductions, explaining who she was, 'A close friend of Chase here, and she virtually lives in his pocket.' She noticed that her host winked, but further greetings intruded and in the general mêlée, the gesture was forgotten.

Attraction of opposites must have been responsible for the joining together of the second couple. Al, the bespectacled husband, offered a shy, 'Hi, there,' and was hard put to string together another two words over the rest of the evening, apparently having previously decided that his wife, Elaine, talked enough for two—or three or four or five, for that matter.

'Gee, I just adore your accent,' the lacquered silver-blonde squealed when Romy made the right social noises. 'And that gorgeous Celtic hair!'

Pushed unwillingly beneath the spotlight while Elaine extolled at length, she felt like an exhibit in a waxworks.

'You should see her hair tied up in string,' Chase drawled when Elaine ran out of super-latives, and Romy flashed him a glance, wary of what might be coming next. It was apparent some kind of reputation had preceded her, and she was fearful Chase had decided to tell tales of her offbeat appearances in the harem suit. She had no wish to be paraded as an oddball, and her fingers curled tightly into her palms. Don't let him make fun, she prayed. In the context of the bay, the silver outfit had been acceptable but not now, not here, in the structured confines of suburbia. Chase did not make fun, in fact he was remarkably serious when he added, 'Or strewn across the pillow.' He had not spoken loudly, but everyone heard and there was a resultant ripple of laughter.

Romy's cheeks grew pink. 'Hey!' she said in protest, but her indignation only made the laughter swell.

How could she defend herself? Good manners prevented her from blurting out to people she barely knew that she did not sleep with the curly-haired stallion who was smiling at her so deliciously, appearing to send all kinds of messages with those clear blue eyes. Romy persuaded herself she was over-reacting. His comment about her hair on the pillow was a joke—wasn't it?

While Stu was organising drinks, Ginette tucked herself in beside Romy on the sofa. 'We've been dying to have a look at you,' she confessed, with such a wide smile that it was

impossible to take offence. Romy recalled how
Chase had sounded wary of their hostess, but
could not understand why. The older woman was
a motherly soul, with a sense of humour. Romy
guessed she would not be averse to some plain
speaking and respected that. 'All we hear from
our gorgeous Mr O'Donoghue is "Romy this,
Romy that",' Ginette told her. 'You've made
quite an impact.'

Astonished by this information, she threw a
questioning look, but her escort had been
cornered by the bubbly Elaine who, judging from
the possessive hand on his arm, had a preference
for tall dark men.

'I'm real pleased you two guys are becoming an
item,' Ginette continued.

'I beg your pardon?'

Stu arrived at that moment with a tray of beer
and wine, so Ginette's hostess duties meant the
subject had to be dropped. Mind buzzing, Romy
sipped the white Riesling, but then Stu began
questioning her about Scotland, and she was too
busy dredging up long forgotten memories to
think deeper about the link which supposedly
existed between her and Chase.

In time he escaped Elaine's clutches, and
Romy was a little perturbed when he came to sit
close beside her, casually interlacing his fingers
with hers. Again she decided she must be over-
reacting. Chase could not guess that the mere
touch of his hand sparked off an intense physical
reaction which dismayed her. The first glass of
wine disappeared like magic, and with the second
she began to relax. Her host and hostess were
nice open people who appeared genuinely happy
to see her, and, after days of her own company,

how good it felt to join in a conversation which was witty and interesting. She was pleased she had accepted Chase's invitation, though she still itched to know exactly what he had told the Beazleys about her ...

Stu was generous with his hospitality, keeping her glass constantly filled, and by the time Ginette ushered everyone through to eat, Romy felt pleasantly mellow. The dining-room was as attractive as the living-room, though far more formal. Oyster-coloured curtains gleamed in the soft glow of concealed lighting and beneath an amber globe sparkling glasses and polished cutlery shone on a rosewood table. At each end of the oval were crescent-shaped dishes of golden button chrysanthemums, while a single larger flower had been tucked into the folded napkin at each place setting. After three weeks of munching muesli on a bare kitchen table, it was like dining at the Ritz. Already the aroma from the hostess trolly Ginette had wheeled in was making Romy's taste buds quiver, and she knew it would be a struggle not to disgrace herself by tucking in too heartily.

Mushrooms stuffed with aubergine salad were served first. Elaine greeted the course with noisy exclamations of delight, and begged the recipe. From the conversation, Romy grasped that the two women spent much of their time in harness; attending the same coffee mornings, the same craft classes, even using the same orthodontist for their children's bridgework. She had been admiring the place mats of heavy cream crochet, and when Elaine paused for breath she used the space to comment to her hostess.

'I'm responsible,' Ginette smiled, accepting

Romy's compliments with a broad smile. She nodded towards a gold-framed collage of trees fashioned from nets and velvets. 'I also embroided that, and wove the wall-hangings in the other room. I have this deep-seated creative urge which it's vital to express if I'm to reach my full potential as a person. I hear you're the same?'

In surprise, Romy shook her head. 'Me? No, I can't sew.'

'But you paint,' Ginette prompted, preparing to serve the main dish of roast duck with prunes. She placed tureens of cartwheeled carrots and chain-linked potatoes on the table. 'Chase told us how dedicated you are, working from morning until night.' Her hostess spoke in tones more suited to describing Michelangelo's efforts on the ceiling of the Sistine Chapel. 'It takes a lot to impress Mr O'Donoghue but, honey, you've managed it.'

'I have?'

She looked across at Chase, but he merely raised a broad shoulder into an infinitesimal shrug.

'I understand you chose to paint your cabin white?' Ginette said chattily, handing round the plates. 'I'm deep into motivation, and colours are significant. White can be interpreted as a fresh beginning.'

'Or it could be virginal white!' hooted Elaine, who apparently found the thought highly amusing.

Romy's cheeks grew pink again. 'I like white,' she protested.

Unexpectedly, Chase came to her aid. 'And so do I.'

'You would, you're emotionally involved,' Ginette interjected.

'Careful, that's a sensitive area,' said Stu, raising his glass to the light to examine the thick plummy red wine he had chosen to accompany the meal. 'What do you think of this poison, Chase?'

The table talk now skittered to wines; wines which came from vineyards not far away. Romy could not help feeling slightly distracted. There was far more here than met the eye. Originally she had presumed she intrigued purely because she was a stranger, but now it seemed otherwise. In everyone's mind she was paired off with Chase, but not as a girlfriend—there had been too many asides, too many innuendoes for her status to be as simple as that. The odd thing was that Chase had been treating her differently all evening. She sensed a subtle change in his attitude, as though he had realised she could amount to more than an attractive oddball, and her mind flew to his reaction earlier, when he had first seen her wearing sophisticated clothes. But surely it was not *just* her appearance which was prompting him to tell the world she was his playmate? She frowned, wryly admitting that there were worse things than being identified as the playmate of a virile Californian, even if the activity was in everyone's imagination!

To all outward appearances, Chase was smitten with her. He had held her hand constantly while they were sitting together on the sofa and now kept glancing at her and smiling—smiles which made her heart flip. Like this, Chase was unstoppable but she knew she could not afford to trust him. She would have felt happier armed with a whip and a chair to keep him at bay.

'How do you like living out on the coast?' Elaine asked her, dabbing a napkin at the corners of her heavily lipsticked mouth. They had just finished a calorie-rich concoction of meringue, fresh fruit and cream, which tasted like heaven.

'I love it,' Romy replied, flashing Chase a glance which warned she was in no danger of weakening over her decision to live in the cabin, though privately she admitted that this was not quite true. During her solitary painting spells, doubts had surfaced. The bay was beautiful, the cabin did have possibilities, but . . .

Ginette's concern came to the fore. 'Honey, it'll be very lonely for you when Chase goes away,' she warned.

'I can cope,' Romy answered brightly.

Chase reached across the table and touched her fingertips. 'But you'll miss me?' He was doing it again, acting like—a lover!

'I expect so.'

Romy took her fingers away. She had no wish to be drawn further into this game of his, yet, for the first time, she realised she *would* miss him— very much. Even though they rarely came into contact, she always knew Chase was there in case of emergencies. How would she feel when he was thousands of miles away? A door slammed in her mind. She would face up to that problem when it arose.

'Maybe I should ask Stu to keep tabs on you while I'm abroad?' he drawled. 'Remind you which side of the road to drive on, or do you still have that crazy notion about getting rid of the Buick?'

'I might,' she announced, her chin jutting to counteract the amusement in his eyes.

'Why don't you drive Chase's Cadillac when he's away?' Ginette suggested.

Romy grinned wickedly. If she was being publicly branded as his girlfriend and more, why not derive a dividend? 'Yes, why don't I? You wouldn't mind that, would you? After all, what's a car between such——' She circled an expressive hand, '—good friends?'

Everyone laughed, except Chase. When he ignored her honey-coated smile, she saw the balance had shifted in her favour. Now was her chance to reap a little revenge. Romy was not armed with the paintbrush, but she sensed she had the upper hand, albeit temporarily. She had not the slightest intention of driving his Cadillac, but Chase was not to know that.

'And I could use your hot tub,' she added. 'Couldn't I, darling?'

He narrowed his eyes at the endearment, recognising he had been hoist with his own petard. 'I guess so,' he agreed.

'Though it's far more fun when we use it together, isn't it, darling?' Romy wondered if she could be going over the top, but she batted her eyelashes disgracefully, enjoying the unusual spectacle of Chase ill at ease.

Stu guffawed. 'I bet it is.'

Elaine claimed Chase's attention with a hand on his wrist. 'What shape swimming pool do you have?' she asked.

'I don't have a pool, only a hot tub.' He could not mask his relief that the woman had rescued him.

'No pool!'

'No room. I live on a hillside, and it would cost the earth to have one installed on the slope.'

Elaine was aghast to think a Californian could exist without a private pool, and was still chattering about the glories of her own backyard and its blue-tiled extravaganza, when they returned to the living-room. 'Summer here without a pool, I don't know how you do it!' she exclaimed.

Chase reached for Romy, his fingers claiming her hand. 'Don't worry,' he drawled. 'I'm having a pool built on Miss MacDonald's land— eventually.'

'And have you chosen the shape?' asked Elaine. She turned her attention to Romy. 'Out here you can choose any one of around, say, forty-eight different pool shapes, and it's real instructive to discover which one people pick. Isn't it, Ginette?'

Their hostess looked up from pouring the coffee. 'Sure is. Like hearts are for romantics,' she explained, when Romy looked puzzled.

Chase's mouth twitched. 'Mine will be phallic,' he announced.

'Yours *would* be!' laughed Stu, slapping his thighs with inelegant delight. Romy kept mute, fearing the conversation was going to slide out of control, but Stu changed the subject. 'How do you like this neighbourhood of ours?' he asked.

'From the little I've seen, it looks very nice,' she told him.

He nodded a happy agreement. 'We're fortunate in that we have strikingly high auto availability.'

'He means you can do everything by car,' Chase said *sotto voce*, acting as interpreter.

'Right on. We have drive-in banks, drive-in

cinemas, drive-in worship,' Stu smiled, proud of the prospect.

'Only the dispossessed wait at bus stops,' Chase whispered in an amused undertone. 'So be warned.' He raised his voice. 'Did you manage to fix the timing on your lawn sprinkler like I told you, Stu?'

'Yeah, thanks. Don't know what I'd do without your practical streak.'

'There is such a thing as being *too* practical,' Ginette intruded, and Romy saw that Chase's jaw tightened for an instant.

When the coffee-pot was empty and the liqueurs drunk, the men went out to inspect the lawn sprinkler, while Romy helped Ginette and Elaine to clear the dining-room table. She was desperate to discover what lay behind all the innuendos, and when Elaine disappeared to refix her face, she grabbed her chance.

'Why did you congratulate me when we first arrived?' Romy asked her hostess, giving a careless laugh which was supposed to indicate that the answer did not matter too much.

Ginette straghtened from stacking plates in the dishwasher. 'Honey, any woman who can persuade Chase O'Donoghue to commit himself deserves congratulations. Poor Julia never managed it in all of seven years. Whoops, me and my big mouth!' she exclaimed, with a grin. 'You *do* know about Julia, I presume?'

'Not much,' Romy confessed. She would discover how Chase was supposed to have committed himself later, for now she would settle for learning more about the blonde.

'Well, maybe I'm telling tales out of school, but he kept poor Julia strung up. Why she didn't have him go take a hike years ago, I'll never know. Yes, I do know,' Ginette adjusted. 'For all his faults, he's one hell of an attractive guy and I guess she loved him. But be warned, honey, don't let him play the same game with you. You get him to that altar double-quick.'

Romy gave an indeterminate bob of her head. Having got this far, it was too late to explain she was Chase's neighbour and nothing more.

'Chase would never admit it, but he needs a wife and a family,' Ginette reprimanded. 'He tries to make out he's so independent, has no need for a woman about the place, but it's all a great big sham. That damned father of his has a lot to answer for, he brought Chase up like a robot.' Romy murmured something vague which the older woman took to be a signal to tell more. 'Paddy was a pleasant enough guy, but he was so *organised*! He was obsessed with being neat and tidy. He'd been through a bad marriage and seemed to imagine that the formula for a trouble-free life was to keep females at a distance. I guess something of that has rubbed off on Chase.' Ginette grinned. 'Paddy hated having women in the house, used to complain like crazy about their high heels marking his carpet. I reckon Julia only survived because she was ultra-orderly herself. Though Chase told me once that his father never did accept her.'

Romy began to feel sorry for the trim blonde. The girl had never been popular with Chase's father, and then appeared to have been given the brush-off after seven years!

'Julia sounds to have had a rough deal.'

'I've always thought so,' Ginette agreed, warming to Romy for her generous spirit. 'She's skipped across country to work at the New York office, so I'm keeping my fingers crossed that she'll find Mr Right, once she's worked Chase out of her system.'

'I hope so.'

For a moment they pondered over the fate of the unfortunate Julia.

'Chase and his father had a good enough relationship, but there were some terrific rows,' her hostess revealed. 'Chase has a hot temper and Paddy's prissy ways used to drive him wild. Mind you, Chase likes to do everything properly himself. You can guarantee that diving ranch of his will be a splendid affair, and very well run.' Scenting danger, Romy kept quiet. 'I expect he's bored you stiff with his plans,' Ginette prattled. 'But it's all so convenient now, isn't it? You and he falling in love. For years, he's been itching to have that land of yours, and this way he won't even have to lay out the cash!'

Romy joined in Ginette's laughter, though hers was synthetic. She felt far from laughing. Whatever devious game Chase O'Donoghue was presently playing he was playing it at her expense. She could not decipher whether or not he was supposed to have proposed marriage, but marriage, or not, he had most certainly compromised her. Romy did not take kindly to having either her present lifestyle, or her future, misrepresented. The green eyes blazed. How dare he!

Her initial reaction was to tell Ginette the plain truth. She paused. Better still, why not wait until everyone was gathered together again and make a grand announcement which would totally annihilate his ego? She thought again. Two could

play games. Why not give him ample supplies of
rope and watch as he hung himself?

'Ginette, those new drapes of yours in the foyer
are so *elegant*!' Elaine carolled, signalling her
return, and Romy listened to the conversation for
a minute or two, before excusing herself.

She found Chase on the sofa, long legs spread
wide apart as he earnestly described snorkelling
techniques to the silent Al.

'If you're physically fit and you can swim,
there's one helluva good time to be had from the
sport. But there are rules,' he added, giving a
quick smile as Romy sat down beside him. 'For a
start you'd be well advised to have a medical
check and make sure there's no high blood
pressure or any other reason why you could black
out in the water. You should never dive when
suffering from a cold, and——'

Romy ran a forefinger along his knee. 'And
what, darling?' she purred.

He turned, his sense of purpose fizzling away
like air out of a balloon, and looked at her. She
saw from his expression how much she had
disturbed him, and she felt powerful.

'And expert advice is vital for the beginner,' he
rattled off.

'Will you teach me?' she murmured. Arching
her back like a cat, Romy stretched slowly and
knew she was tantalising him with the outline of
her firm high breasts.

For a moment Chase seemed mesmerised, then
he grinned. 'Kiddo, I'll teach you everything.'

Romy had thought she would outwit him, play
him at his own game, but she had been wrong.
Chase was far too clever. His surprise at her
display of sensual affection was brief, and the

evening rapidly showed signs of running completely off the rails. He seemed to believe he had
been given the go-ahead to make public love and
though, at first, Romy attempted to backtrack
and maintain some poise, she was fighting a
losing battle. As a predatory male, Chase was
dynamite. She could find no weapons with which
to resist, and began to understand why Julia had
hung around for seven long years.

He slung his arm around her shoulders to hold
her close, so close that his jaw brushed her hair
and she could smell the lime-lemon of his
cologne. True, Chase contributed pleasantly to
the general conversation, but there were many
intimate asides which he whispered, his breath
warm against her ear. When he kissed her brow,
Romy began to melt, and by the time he decreed
they must leave, she was as liquid as a puddle on
the floor.

Al and Elaine also departed at the same time,
so there were noisy thanks, hugs and handshakes,
car doors slamming in the general exodus. The
wink Ginette gave said she expected a wedding
invitation, and soon. They drove away, and
Chase's concentration and the darkness in the
Cadillac, gave Romy the opportunity to pull
herself together. The pressure of temper began to
build again. His behaviour this evening meant
she was due an explanation *and* an apology, but
minutes passed and it became clear Chase was not
about to offer either.

'Well?' she demanded, unable to hold back any
longer.

'Well what?'

He was relaxed, long fingers spread easily as he
controlled the wheel. They had left the trappings

of suburbia, and were now heading through dark lanes towards the coast. Romy gave his right profile a look which shot like an arrow.

'Well, what was this evening's charade all about? How dare you introduce me to your friends under false pretences! Thanks to you, I'm now thought to be, to be——' She began to splutter. 'To be your lover or something.'

'Not something. Lover, period.'

'But I'm not!' she snapped back.

'You'd like to be.' He was twisting the conversation back to front. 'And I'd like it too. I had a helluva job sitting still back there, I wanted you so much.' He gave a sidelong glance through the dark and laughed. 'Ginette will be forced to revise her opinions. She's always considered me a cool customer, heartless even, where women are concerned, but after tonight's performance, all that will be changed. I've proved myself to be as star-struck as the next man. I could hardly keep my hands off you, and she knew it!'

Romy was getting madder by the minute. How dare he confuse the issue by talk of lovemaking and wanting her?

'But that's all it was—a *performance*!'

'It might have started out as one, but it ended up differently, didn't it? You were as aroused as I was,' he said comfortably.

'*I was not!*'

'Kiddo, I don't like to contradict, but that body of yours spoke a language which was mighty powerful.' Chase chuckled. 'Don't be so hard on yourself, it's no sin to admit to natural desires.'

'God! You're unbelievable.' Romy was waving her hands around. 'Why? Just tell me why you made the Beazleys think we're going—going to be married?'

'I didn't actually say that. I hinted we were going to join forces, and Ginette's imagination provided the rest.' His voice changed and he became serious. 'Maybe I shouldn't have deceived them, but when I was over at their place last week Ginette started riling me about doing the decent thing by Julia. It's an old ploy, and usually I take it in my stride but, for some stupid reason, I lost my temper. I got so uptight that I revealed how Julia and I had decided to call it a day.' He shook his head at his stupidity. 'I should have known better than to reveal all to Ginette!' Chase lifted a hand from the wheel, in a weary gesture. 'But I told her the truth, and she was on me like a garlic milkshake. She got real heavy.'

Romy was trying to keep track. 'Where does Julia fit into all this?' she questioned, wary he might be deliberately confusing her.

'We had an arrangement whereby every time I returned home on repat, we'd meet up and spend time together. It was based on sex,' he said carelessly, 'and it suited her as much as it suited me. Marriage wasn't an ingredient, never had been, but try telling Ginette that! She has this fixation about women finding fulfilment only in marriage, so when I explained that Julia had been offered a plum job in New York and was over the moon, she refused to believe me. She was convinced I'd given Julia her walking papers.' Chase gave a wry laugh. 'I saw red. I decided that if Ginette was so convinced I was a mean bastard, then I'd damn well *be* a mean bastard. It was irrational, I know, but—but I told her I'd split with Julia because I'd met another girl.'

'Me?'

'You were handy.'

'Thanks!'

'Ginette was so smug,' he recalled. 'At one and the same time she was able to pat herself on the back because she'd been right all along about what a bastard I really am, and yet she was thrilled to discover that the bastard has a heart.'

'But you don't!' Romy slammed back. 'You've involved me in this stupid situation without a single thought about me. All that mattered was *you*!'

The Cadillac had been eating up the miles, and now they left the country road and were driving along the hilltop track towards the bay.

'There's no harm done,' he coaxed. 'Besides, I did lend you the ladder and start clearing your backyard, *and* you ruined my shirt and pants. I reckon you owe me one, kiddo.'

His justification took her breath away. 'So you think you have the right to parade me in public as your—your mistress?' she hissed.

'Don't be so dramatic, and stop flicking your fingers in front of my face. You'll make us have an accident.'

With deliberate effort, Romy knotted her hands in her lap. 'What happens when it becomes obvious to the Beazleys that we are not going to join forces?'

He shrugged, swinging the Cadillac on to the lane. As they approached the double garage, Chase operated a gadget and the doors rolled up by remote control. He drove the big car under cover and braked. It was a slick operation. Come to think of it, most things Chase did were slick, too damned slick!

'I'll work something out,' he said, climbing from the driving seat.

'And you don't care about the way you've—you've maligned me?' she demanded, as she followed him on to the lane. The magic doors rolled shut.

'You'll be gone by then.' It was a give-away remark, but when they drew level with his door, he took hold of her elbow. 'Come in and have a drink,' he suggested. 'A nightcap.'

'No!'

'Playing hard to get?' he drawled, arching a brow, and she saw his mouth crease into a grin in the darkness.

'It's not that at all.' Romy stopped speaking when she realised the implications of her words. She folded her arms and glared. The night was silver and black, the shine of a full moon glimmering across the inky stretch of the sea. In another mood, she would have admitted it was a night for romance. 'I'm sick and tried of you running my life for me,' she protested, ignoring the way the shadows had sculpted the intensely male lines of his face into those of an Aztec warrior.

'You can bawl me out indoors, kiddo.'

Before she could stop him, Chase had gripped her elbow and was steering her through the side door, along the patio and into the elegant lounge. He bent to snap on a couple of table lamps, their golden light filling the room with a welcoming glow.

'That's typical,' she stormed, hands on hips, chest heaving from her enforced march into the house. 'I have to do what *you* want to do.'

Chase stepped forward and put his arms around her.

'But you want it too,' he murmured, and bent
his head. Tenderly his lips brushed hers,
touching, then not touching, playing over the soft
fullness of her mouth for a long delicious
agonising moment which made it pure bliss when
he increased the pressure into a kiss. Chase was
right, she *did* want what he wanted. Her protest,
palms flat against his chest, was a token gesture
for, as the kiss strengthened, so her hands stilled
until she was sliding them around his neck, her
body unconsciously arching to his. His physical
positive far outweighed her mental negative to
what he was doing. Her lips parted and she
sighed as he invaded her mouth, hotly and
moistly, his tongue entwining with hers. 'Baby,'
he murmured.

Kiss followed kiss. Mouths clinging, he pulled
her down on to the white leather sofa, cradling
her, stroking her hair, his hands moving, fondling
and caressing until her skin began to burn, and
the blood streamed through her veins like blast-
furnace gold. She was so hot, so molten, that it
seemed only natural for Chase to begin to
undress her. He slid open the buttons on her silk
shirt, raising her to tug the garment free of her
trousers, and she made no protest when he
removed the lacy wisp of her bra, his hands
claiming the seductive curves of her full breasts.

'You're so beautiful,' he murmured, touching
the sensitive peaks with his fingertips until Romy
felt as if she was spinning out of orbit. Chase
pulled at his own shirt, tossing it aside to hold
her against him, arousing her with the scour of
his hair-sprinkled chest against her nipples.
Romy flung back her head, teeth clenched as she
savoured the torment of his naked flesh against

hers. 'Baby,' he said brokenly into her throat. 'Baby. I—oh God!' Chase's breathing was shallow, as fevered as hers. 'Oh God, what are you doing to me?' His hands moved down to grind her into his thighs. 'I want you.' He sounded angry, as though he resented being out of control. 'I've never felt like this before.'

Before. The word struck a chord. Before meant Julia, seven years of Julia. Seven years when all Chase required from a relationship was sex! Romy's temperature cooled as rapidly as if a cloud had covered the sun, and she jammed her hands against his chest, separating them.

'Haven't you?' Her voice dripped icicles, making Chase sit up to rake a bewildered hand through his dishevelled curls. 'I thought it was a regular occurrence. What was the arrangement with Julia? Three times a week, Mondays, Wednesdays and Fridays, with maybe a matinee on Saturdays?' she sneered. 'But you're forgetting something, Chase. I'm not Julia, content to service you, as and when required. Purely recreational, emotions not involved.'

For a moment Romy thought he was going to strike her as pure wrath blazed in his eyes, but then he swept to his feet, furiously flinging on his shirt.

'I might have guessed,' he snarled. 'You're just a younger version of Ginette and I'm back to being the bastard. How come it's *me* who's at fault when we were both contributing to what was happening just a moment ago, and earlier this evening?' Chase broke off to give a harsh laugh, glaring at her as she retrieved her clothes. 'I'm straightforward about sex, but it's wedding bells you're interested in, and doubtless you'll be

prepared to barter. I've met girls like you before.'
He started to mimic. '*Tell me you care and I'll let
you touch me, but if you want to go all the way, you
must produce a certificate—of marriage!*'

The ugliness of his tone made her wince, but
Romy tried not to care. Roughly she tucked her
shirt back into her tousers. 'Aren't you forgetting
something?' she demanded. 'You've mentioned
sex and you've mentioned marriage, but what
about the vital ingredient—love?'

He curled his lip. 'My ad-lib translation for
love is a diamond ring to flash around, a fancy
villa which will impress the girlfriends, and a
regular pay packet coughed up by some poor
sucker.'

'That's a very cynical attitude.'

Chase shrugged. 'Don't forget, I'm older than
you so maybe I have a firmer grip on reality.'

'No way.' Romy jabbed a finger. 'Your ideas
don't impress me one bit. Okay, hide behind that
brittle facade, but before too long you'll have
rhinocerous skin. You didn't mention love,
because love scares you.'

He laughed at the idea. 'Scares me?'

'It's true. You'll sit up here in this immaculate
house indulging in shallow little romances for the
rest of your life, because you aren't brave enough
to risk becoming involved. But you'll miss out,
Chase! Okay, so you won't have the agony, but
neither will you have the ecstasy.' Romy's finger
had taken on a life of its own, sketching furiously.
Her cheeks were flushed, her hair tumbling
around her face. 'You and Julia sound to have
been ideally suited. Both inhibited egotists who
aren't warm enough, or brave enough, to open up
and fall in love. How the hell could you? Seven

years!' She made a massive expressive swoop with both hands and nearly knocked a table lamp flying.

'You're wrong.' A nerve was jumping in Chase's temple. 'We were very fond of each other.'

'Fond—ha!'

'And you're wrong about my future. 'I won't be sitting up here alone, because I'll be busy and content, running my diving ranch.'

'Over my dead body,' Romy intervened. 'I'll make certain you don't get your hands on my land—ever!'

CHAPTER SIX

HER head thumping, Romy stalked down through the inky blackness, knowing Chase kept guard higher up the hill until she was safely indoors, though whether he needed to satisfy himself she was safe, or whether he was thinking, 'Good riddance', she could not tell. Muttering beneath her breath about his shortcomings, she washed, undressed and flung herself into bed, but sleep proved elusive. Traitorous thoughts began to float in and out of her head as her anger seeped away. If only Chase had the capacity to fall in love, what a wonderful partner he could be! She suspected that deep down he was terrified of being vulnerable, for wasn't his need to keep his home in rigid order, to dominate the objects around him, a sign of this? Romy stared through the darkness, listening to the distant splash of the waves. She smiled ruefully. And wasn't she in danger of becoming a home-grown analyst, like Ginette?

How close she had been to giving herself to him! Locked in his arms, there had been a moment when she had wondered if she was falling in love, but the idea was pathetic. She must need her head examining! Chase's goal was to have her sell him the cabin, and his apparent wooing must be viewed from that standpoint. She was deceiving herself if she thought he genuinely cared tuppence about her. And if he ever guessed how susceptible she was to his particular brand of virile masculinity, he would use her, taking but never giving and, regardless of the cabin, Romy knew how fatal it would be if she allowed herself to become involved. She could not cope with the kind of one-way relationship Chase would offer.

She began to wonder how she could manage to live with him so near at hand. He was mad at her right now, offended by her character assassination, but suppose he did an about-turn? The idea frightened and excited her. Romy knew her hormones could betray her into winding up in his bed. A cautionary voice told her to leave California, and fast!

She tossed and turned. Much as the prospect of Chase in residence higher up the hill troubled her, so the thought of him disappearing abroad also made her fret. So far the days had been long, mainly sunlit and pleasant, but winter was around the corner. Romy pictured the bay in the dark and cold, herself the sole occupant. What would she do if a knock came at her door late one night when the wind was howling off the Pacific? She was miles from habitation, and even if she rang the police, they would take a long time to reach her—too long. Chase's property was secure, hers was not. Any strong man—a burglar, a down-and-out, a rapist, could barge through the feeble locks.

Her misgivings grew. Basically, she did not enjoy living alone. Romy needed people. It wasn't that she required non-stop gossip, or to be forever in a crowd, but she was a companionable soul and enjoyed sharing—comments, laughs, experiences. Now she admitted that her weeks in California had too often smacked of solitary confinement. Yet curiously, she was growing to

love the bay. Its appeal had caught at her heart-
strings, and she felt tugged in opposite directions.
But how much of the attraction relied on Chase
living up the hill? Oh God, was she becoming
dependent on him? As dawn streaked the sky,
Romy reached a decision. She would sell the
cabin and depart.

Despite the statement she had hurled earlier,
she was tempted to capitulate and simply offer
the property to Chase. For a long time she argued
with herself over this. His enthusiasm for the
proposed diving ranch was strong and genuine,
yet why should he have everything his own way?
She recalled Ginette's phrase. Wouldn't Chase
have a better chance of 'reaching his full potential
as a person', if he learned to adapt, to bend? If he
could be persuaded to loosen up over his plans
and compromise by fitting the ranch *around* the
cabin, might he not learn to loosen up in other
ways?

After breakfast Romy leafed through the
Yellow Pages, rang the office of the first real
estate agent listed and, by noon, was opening the
door to an officious grey-haired lady.

'Mrs Mirabelle Brooks,' she announced, marching into the house, a navy trouser-suited
soldier armed with briefcase and clipboard. She
planted two stout brogues in the centre of the
livng-room floor and looked around, her eyes
sweeping over the interior as mercilessly as a
lighthouse beacon. 'I must be frank, and tell you
from the start that there's little demand for this
type of property. It's too far from town. Do you
have a garage?'

'No.'

'Carport?'

'No.'

'How do you heat this place?'

'Er, there's a couple of electric fires.'

'Sounds grim. Is there a pool?'

'I'm afraid not.'

Mrs Brooks was marking crosses on the sheet clipped to her board, and when every one of her questions demanded a negative, Romy's spirits began to tumble.

'Wouldn't the cabin sell as a weekend retreat or holiday home?' she suggested, standing aside as the woman marched back and forth measuring dimensions.

'We might interest some crank who's hot on ornithology,' Mrs Brooks mused, peering out at the ocean were seagulls wheeled and dipped over the sunlit waters. 'But even for weekends, most clients prefer gracious living these days. That yard would make lumberjacks quake.'

'I'm hoping to make some headway with the garden this week,' Romy said at speed, wondering how she could tackle the work alone. With their relationship in ruins, Chase would not offer any further help. 'And I shall finish painting the fence.'

The woman frowned. 'I'd replace that, honey, if I were you.'

'And I'm intending to decorate inside,' Romy rushed on with a waft of her arms, willing to scatter rose petals if necessary. That morning she had fled around the cabin, cleaning and tidying like a creature possessed. She had been impressed with her efforts, but unhappily realised her visitor was not.

'Waste of time decorating,' Mrs Brooks announced. 'Clients prefer to choose their own decor. Been here long?'

'About a month. The property was left to me by a relative.'

'And you'd rather have the cash?' It was obvious Mrs Brooks was making a rapid reassessment. 'I was wondering how you came to be out here in the sticks. I thought maybe you were a nature freak.'

Romy was offended. Not because she had been personally maligned, but because the woman had derided the bay. Romy felt protective about the bay. 'You don't have to be a nature freak to enjoy life out here,' she protested hotly. 'Just because there aren't many trimmings like department stores and taxis, it doesn't mean life isn't pleasant. I consider it a privilege to have private access to the sand and the sea. The air is fresh and clear, and——'

'And your roof needs fixing, and the kitchen is antique,' Mrs Brooks pointed out, not unkindly. 'I agree the place does have some charm, but my clients put essentials first. However, I'll do my best. I'll call you before I bring any interested folks out here. Are there any hours I should avoid?'

'None. I'm here all day.' All day and every day, Romy thought wryly. With the garden to clear and the fence to paint, she was due for another stint of solitary confinement.

When Mrs Brooks departed, driving cautiously up the hill in her big car, Romy stood on the verandah to chew over the facts. The real estate agent's verdict was that disposing of the cabin could take months, if not years! So why not swallow her pride and hand over to Chase, lock, stock and barrel? But still she itched to teach him a lesson. He had planned his life with a ruler and set-square, and Romy felt a spasm of satisfaction at knowing she had the power to make a wiggly line. By selling the cabin to a third party, wouldn't she really be doing him a favour? Wouldn't it be character-building if he was forced into considering alternative sitings for his ranch? She decided to go ahead and see what progress Mrs Brooks made in the short-term.

Much to her surprise, the real estate agent called that same afternoon to say a client had materialised, but when he came out to the cabin Romy's delight was quickly tempered.

'Fantastic, fantastic,' he enthused, chewing gum as she followed him and a measurement-quoting Mrs Brooks through one room after another. Dressed like a garage mechanic, he appeared to have crawled from beneath a car only minutes ago, and he said, 'Fantastic,' when he saw the fence, and even *smiled* at the tangled mass of undergrowth. 'You have a fantastic place there,' he called through the car window, as he was driven away, but Romy knew she had seen the last of him. However, some interest on the very first day was promising, and she returned to paint the fence, hoping desperately that Chase had been out on his patio and had seen the action. A strange car would have been bound to make him curious, and he was too intelligent not to grasp that an inspection of the property signified it was for sale, but not to him!

For a while Romy was on tenterhooks, wondering if he would telephone, or stride down for an eyeball-to-eyeball confrontation, but her fears were groundless. No irate fireball hurtled from above. Indeed, she never even caught sight of him in the distance, nor heard the Cadillac purring in or out of his garage. Darkness fell, and when the familiar lights did not glow on his patio, she decided Chase must have driven into San Francisco to round up a replacement Julia from a singles bar. That would not take long. When he chose to release that sexual charge, Romy doubted any woman on earth could find the strength to resist.

Her nerves leapt when the telephone rang early next day. Romy rapidly assembled the carefully prepared explanation of her actions, and then decided she did not need to explain. The property was hers, and she could do exactly what she wished with it. She swallowed hard. This had to be Chase—or could it be Mrs Brooks, asking if she could bring along another client? Both prospects had her heart thumping and she was disappointed when her caller turned out to be Mrs Klein. The old lady sounded relieved when she broke the news of the sale.

'I knew you'd come to your senses,' she announced, cheerful for once, though after a few minutes' chatter, she was compelled to close on a note of doom. 'Don't expect a quick sale. Personally, I have my doubts about *anyone* wishing to buy the property.'

Two days passed by. Romy finished the fence and began work on clearing the garden, adding to the waiting bonfire until it reached towering proportions. She was thrashing at the brambles, with little care for life or limb, thinking how Chase was still noticeably absent, when it occured to her that maybe the reason for his silent house was because he had already departed on his next diving assignment. She hit out viciously.

'The louse!' she exclaimed out loud. Living alone was conducive to solitary declarations, and Romy had noticed how, of late, she was talking to herself with remarkable regularity. Maybe she should buy a cat or two, to share her conversations! 'Even if he resents me, he could at least have been neighbourly enough to say goodbye,' she grumbled.

The prospect of Chase being long gone was depressing. It certainly took the edge off her satisfaction when a young Mexican couple arrived to view the cabin. Admittedly, at first glance they said it was not at all what they had anticipated, but Romy would have been content with an unfruitful visit, had Chase been glowering down from his patio. When Mrs Klein phoned later in the day and repeated her invitation to join them in Oakland, Romy was almost tempted to accept. What was she proving by remaining at the cabin? Mrs Brooks could easily be provided with a spare key and left to show clients around alone.

'Maybe I'll come next week,' she told the old lady. 'Once I have the garden in order.' But when she returned to the green labyrinth and assessed what little headway had actually been made, she decided next *year* would have been more appropriate. Flashing secateurs like castanets, she had launched herself into the thickets and was clipping madly, when the telephone rang again. Romy swore beneath her breath, but not wishing to miss Mrs Brooks, and maybe a buyer, she had no option but to wrench herself free, leaving a strip of silver cloth caught amidst the thorns, and gallop for the house.

'Hello,' she panted, grabbing the phone. A

prickle was stuck in the pad of her thumb, and she winced.

'It's me, Chase.' He sounded so distant that, for a split second, she imagined he was ringing from abroad. 'Would you get on over here?'

'To the house?'

'Yes.'

'Now?'

'*Yes!*' Romy sucked at her thumb and the prickle came free. I'm busy, she thought defiantly, and, in any case, I'm not prepared to dance to his tune. She had opened her mouth, ready to make a tart refusal, when he added, 'I'd be real grateful if you would.'

Cursing herself for being all kinds of a fool, she climbed the hill. She had expected Chase to be waiting courteously at the side door, but the door was closed and when she turned the handle, it was locked.

'Terrific, he asks me to come up here, then leaves me kicking my heels outside!' she fumed, pounding on the wood with the palm of her hand. Two minutes she would allow, and then she was off. No way was she at Chase O'Donoghue's beck and call. Meticulously she checked the time and when the second hand crested twice she turned and started for home.

'Romy, wait.'

She had almost reached the cabin when she heard his plea, and she swivelled, tempted to make a brusque sign with two fingers and flounce away, but something in his stance caught her attention. She frowned. Chase was leaning dejectedly against the wall, his whole attitude screaming, 'Help me.'

For a second time she strode up the hill,

despising herself for answering his appeal so readily, but when she drew close her green eyes darkened with concern.

'What's the matter, Chase? Are you ill?'

She had never seen him in such a state. He was untidy, the black curls tousled, a blue sheen of beard indicating that days had passed by since his last shave. His face was drawn, with dark rings around his eyes, and from all appareances his crumpled tee-shirt and shorts had been jogged in and slept in. Romy's gaaze fell to his bare left leg. Chase was holding it awkwardly off the ground, like a dog favouring a limp. The ankle was swollen and distorted. He had to make a conscious effort before he could speak. 'I've damaged my leg, and I think maybe I have flu, or malaria, or I'm hyperventilating or something. I feel lousy.'

'Have you called the doctor?'

'I don't need a doctor, I'm all right.' He did not notice he was contradicting himself. Chase closed his eyes and opened them again, but his gaze was dull.

Romy took control. 'You must go inside and lie down. Put your arm around me and I'll help you.'

She manoeuvred him across the patio and into the house. When she pushed open the door of his bedroom, she stared in amazement. Romy had never seen such a mess, it looked as if a bomb had hit it. Crumpled sheets were strewn half on, half off the bed, pillows lay here and there amidst discarded shoes and socks. In corners she noticed remnants of what had obviously been an attempt at a meal, there were dirty plates and empty cups. On the carpet a pile of soggy towels lay in the centre of a darkly spreading puddle. When she helped him on to the bed, Chase slumped wearily, allowing her to straighten the sheets and plump up a pillow behind his head.

'Thanks,' he groaned.

'When did your hurt your ankle?' she enquired, thinking that from the state of the room he appeared to have been holed up there for weeks.

'Three days ago, I guess.'

'Three days, and you've been here all that time with no help?' she said, irritated by his stupidity.

With great care, Chase stretched out his legs. 'It's only a sprain. I've been wrapping cold compresses around to try and stop the swelling.' He glanced at the towels and the sodden circle of carpet. 'I expected it to clear up.'

Romy was exasperated. 'God, you're so damned self-sufficient! You don't need a doctor. You don't need anybody.'

Chase closed his eyes. 'I need you,' he said.

The doctor arrived an hour after Romy's phone call. He was a thin ascetic man with a goatee beard, who saw nothing strange in her moth-eaten harem suit, and who took it for granted she was part of the household.

'That man of yours deserves a sharp rap over the knuckles,' he informed her, after he had given Chase a thorough examination. 'Some guys just won't accept there's a process called ageing. He's not eighteen any more and it's high time he accepted that. I gather he sets himself some impossibly high target for this morning jog of his, and, come hell or high water, he'll reach it. He went over on his ankle a couple of miles from home but carried on running, determined to meet

some self-imposed schedule.' The doctor shook
his head in despair. 'He might deserve a badge
for courage, but he doesn't get one for common
sense. He's chewed up the muscle good and
proper. Then he lies here, gets a mild fever and
becomes dehydrated into the bargain. It's a
blessing you arrived and made him see sense.'

'How long will it be before he's able to walk?'
Romy asked, showing the doctor to the side door.

'He must have four days minimum in bed, then
use crutches until the muscle strengthens. I'll call
round with some crutches later. Luckily he's so
damn fit that he won't be out of action too long.
I've given an injection to clear the swelling.' He
grinned at her. 'He's a stubborn cuss. You'll have
your work cut out keeping him horizontal, but do
your best. Any problems, give me a call.'

Chase was fast asleep when she returned to the
bedroom, so Romy moved around quietly,
opening the windows to freshen the air and
carrying off the litter. A trail of debris stretched
from the bedroom, via hall and lounge, to the
kitchen. She wondered how Paddy O'Donoghue
would have reacted; from all accounts he would
have gone berserk! A conglomeration of unread
newspapers were thrown out, and she washed all
the dirty cups and plates. Afterwards, she noticed
how the pot plants were drooping, so grabbed the
kettle and began working her way around.

'What are you doing with that?' Chase
enquired sleepily, waking up as she had sneaked
back into his bedroom to attend to a spreading
pink-blossomed begonia on the dressing table.

'I couldn't find the proper spray, but I'm
watering the plants. And I'll water you, if you
start bossing me around.' Romy swung the kettle

in his direction and giggled when a dollop
unexpectedly shot from the spout and landed on
his chest.

'Great!' he said, gazing down at the darkening
patch. 'Here I am, about to expire, and you're
intent on drowning me.' He certainly did not give
the impression of being about to expire. Already
the nasty pallor had gone from his face, and a
glance at the bandaged ankle confirmed the
swelling was beinning to subside.

'It's bathtime,' she grinned, as he put his full
weight on his arms to ease himself up on to the
pillow. Romy surveyed the crumpled jogging
gear. 'From the look of that lot, a cycle in the
washing machine would do no harm. How about
stripping off?'

Chase grinned. 'Kiddo, I've been waiting such
a long time for you to ask me that!' For an
invalid, he was showing a remarkably sturdy
sense of humour, but she decided it would be
prudent to skirt around the comment.

'What I meant was, if you change into your
pyjamas, I'll sling your dirty clothes and those
wet towels, into the machine.'

'I can't manage to change all by myself, you'll
have to undress me,' he replied, an impudent
gleam in his blue eyes, but when she swung the
kettle in his direction, he cringed back. 'Okay,
okay,' he agreed, eyeing her warily. 'I'll cope.'

'Good. I'm off to make some lunch, and when
I return I expect to find a pile of dirty clothes
waiting to be washed,' Romy told him, and with
another teasing swing of the kettle, she departed.

His fridge was well-stocked. She prepared
mushroom omelette, adding a cheese and chive

topping, then filled dishes with butterscotch ice-cream for dessert. Chase was wearing maroon pyjama trousers when she carried in the tray, through she saw he was bare-chested. Off-colour he might be, and no longer eighteen, but still Romy found it difficult to concentrate on her food. Somehow her eyes had a compulsion to wander over the well-developed muscles, with their coating of dark hair. His skin was so tanned, so firm, that her fingers tingled with the desire to reach out and touch the hard contours.

'You must rest now,' she said, when they had finished eating, and knew she sounded like a brisk staff nurse. 'I'll deal with the chores, and later I'll come back to prepare your dinner and check that you're okay for the night.'

'You can't leave me,' he protested. 'Lock up the cabin and move in here. There's a guest room.' His blue look hooked on to hers. 'You're perfectly safe. I'm in no position to leap on you, but suppose I fell during the night? You wouldn't like to think of me expiring here alone?'

She clicked her tongue in exasperation. 'You've already been alone for three days, Chase. Expecting a night nurse is overdue. I'm sure you can manage.' She cast a glance at his neatly strapped ankle. As far as she could tell, it was well on its way back to normality.

'Maybe I can, but I don't want to.' Chase wiggled his toes experimentally. 'I get lonely, don't you?' She nodded, feeling the tug of his argument. More solitary hours held little attraction. 'So join me, just until I can walk again,' he coaxed.

Tempted, Romy sighed, but then she remembered Mrs Brooks. Good grief, her home had been unoccupied for hours, and maybe the phone had been ringing. 'I need to be at the cabin in case of visitors,' she protested, relieved to have found an excuse.

'Be realistic, Romy. You don't have friends around here, so who in the hell's going to call? If you're scared about missing the Avon lady, pin a note to the door telling her to come up here,' he replied, gently mocking.

Against all her doubts, Romy allowed herself to be persuaded to spend the night in his guest room. She cleared away the lunch tray and left him to rest, but the minute her chores were completed, she rushed back down the hill to telephone the real estate agent. Mrs Brooks advised that no prospective buyers were on the horizon, but nonetheless Romy passed over Chase's phone number, stressing she could return to the cabin at a moment's notice.

When she replaced the receiver, she grew thoughtful. Before contacting Mrs Brooks, she had first checked that Chase's telephone was installed in the kitchen, where she could reach it first. With his gammy ankle he had no chance of intercepting any message, so she was safe on that score. Yet honesty seemed to demand she reveal what was afoot. In her imagination Romy had seen his deducing for himself that she was selling the cabin to an outsider, and now she shied away from blurting out her intention, face to face. If he had come storming down, spitting daggers, she would have been able to storm back, but she did not see how she could tell him 'cold', so to speak. Not when he was ill in bed, and being so damned pleasant! The timing was all wrong. A temptation pricked to ring back Mrs Brooks and cancel the sale, but her previous arguments against this began to bubble. She would let matters ride, for a day or two at least. Disposing of the cabin promised to be a long drawn out affair, so she had plenty of time if she wanted to change her mind . . .

Romy cast aside her silver suit in preference for a more respectable tailored lilac shirt and designer jeans and, after packing an overnight bag, she locked the cabin and retraced her steps. Chase was asleep when she returned. He had confessed how painful his leg had been, so painful that for the past three days all he had managed was a fitful slumber, drifting in and out of consciousness, but now he was able to catch up.

Once she had installed herself in the guest room, ironed the freshly dried clothes and planned dinner, Romy had a scout around. How pleasant it felt to be back in comfortable and well-furnished surroundings! By contrast, the cabin's meagre facilities seemed positively anti-diluvian. Chase awoke for dinner, but afterwards drifted off to sleep, and so she browsed contentedly through his bookshelves and listened to records, taking great care to return everything to its proper place at the end of the evening. When Chase surfaced, she brewed coffee and saw he was settled for the night, though she refused the goodnight kiss he requested. After showering, Romy tumbled into bed and slept solidly for eight hours.

Only when she awoke, bright-eyed and bushy-tailed, did she realise how rarely she enjoyed a good night's sleep. At the cabin unexplained noises disturbed her, probably something as simple as gulls on the roof, or undergrowth brushing against the verandah, but they were disturbances which shocked her out of sleep. Romy had never consciously accepted she could be frightened, but now she began to wonder. In Chase's house she was safe from the things that go bump in the night, though whether she was safe from her host—or her own treacherous desires—was a different matter.

At her bidding, Chase stayed in bed all the next day, but by evening he was restless, eager to experiment on the crutches the doctor had delivered.

'Orders are that you have two more days horizontal,' Romy protested, when she found him sitting on the side of the bed.

'Then you come and be horizontal with me.'

'No!' She kept well back, near the wall.

'Don't be cross.'

'I'm not.'

Chase put his head to one side. 'You sound it. Why do you have this hang-up about——' He spread his hands. '—About us getting close? Together we'd make the world vibrate, you know that, don't you?'

Her heart began to race. 'No, I don't know any such thing,' Romy replied. 'And it's not me that has a hang-up, it's you!'

'Me?' he laughed, half quizzical. 'I want to make love to you, it's as simple as that. You're a great-looking broad, with a lovely figure, and I like you.'

'You like me—big deal!'

He recoiled from the harshness of her tone. 'I like you a helluva lot,' he protested, sounding hurt. 'When I was lying here alone I couldn't get you out of my mind.' He bent down to tug at the white crepe bandage, choosing not to meet her eyes. 'That evening at Stu's was amazing. I hardly knew where I was at. You took my breath away, and believe me, that was a new sensation.'

'One you never had in seven years with Julia?' she slammed back, her green eyes blazing. Chase did not seem to realise they were talking about two entirely different things. Love was on Romy's mind, but all he could think about was sex!

'To hell with Julia, that was entirely different. She's a mature career woman who knows exactly where she's going, and what she wants from life.'

'And I don't, because in your book I'm—I'm capricious?' Romy was fizzing. How *could* he compare her unfavourably with that ice-cool blonde?

'Did I say that?' Chase raised his eyes to hers and licked his lips, a strangely uncertain gesture. 'You're warm, Romy, and spontaneous and human. And at times you frighten the living daylights out of me.' He went back to fuss with the bandage.

Romy was stopped in her tracks. For once he had been candid, sounding vulnerable. Dare she believe Chase was prepared to lower his defences? A mishmash of emotions filled her head—love, wonder, desire, doubt, bewilderment. He raised his head and grinned, seeming to recognise she was struggling with an inward dilemma. When he stretched out his hand, she found herself walking forward, allowing him to capture her as he lifted her fingers to his lips and kissed them. She sat down beside him on the bed.

'But *you* frighten *me*,' she said. 'You know the right way to go about so many things, like painting or fixing lawn sprinklers. I feel inadequate by comparison. You're a perfectionist, Chase, always in control.'

'What did you say—big deal? I might be fine where practicalities are concerned, but I'm not quite so clever emotionally. Ginette's been telling me to let go, hang loose, for years, and the other night you said the same thing. Maybe you have a point. I suppose I have tended to keep away from involvements.' He looked across and saw that Julia's name was on her lips. '*Love* involvements!' he said impatiently, irritated at having been obliged to say the word.

Suddenly Romy felt lighthearted. 'Oh, *that!*' she grinned, tossing her head.

At her smile, his anger fell away and Chase bent to touch her cheek, feeling the silky skin smooth and warm beneath his fingertips.

'Romy,' he sighed in anguish, and fell on her like a loving wolf, pulling her down with him on to the bed. His mouth was hot and fevered, parting her lips to invade her senses with a rapacious desire. The amalgam of freewheeling sensuality and tortured emotion which jarred within him, fascinated her. Romy wanted to know him properly, on all levels, but at this moment the physical level mattered most. The erratic beat of her heart made a mockery of her wish to escape him. How wonderful it was to be held in his arms, to be stroked and caressed, to be cherished. As his kisses lengthened, she felt a change deep within him. His first urgency gave way to a newer, stronger emotion. Masterful and experienced, Chase was also tender, wanting to give her pleasure, wanting her to share. This isn't just sex, she thought in some dim corner of her mind, it *has* to be more. His lips moved to the vee of her blouse, kissing the soft skin, edging the silk aside until the swell of her breasts was revealed. She sobbed when he pulled the white lace free, and the fiery globes were taut and straining beneath the moist caress of his mouth. More, she thought dizzily, I want more, so much more. The feel of his lips, his mouth covering the rosy aureoles was driving her insane.

When a telephone rang close by, Romy groaned. Not now, she felt like pleading, not now. Not now. Her brow furrowed. Wasn't the phone in the kitchen? Why did it sound so loud?

'Oh hell.' Chase reluctantly raised his head, complaining when the ringing did not stop. He gulped in deep breaths, and began to edge them both towards the side of the bed. Nestled against his shoulder, Romy kept her eyes closed, refusing to surface, only wanting him to return to their lovemaking. Hard muscles rolled beneath her head when Chase stretched out an arm. 'Hi,' he said, and quoted his number. Drugged with desire, she wondered how he could sound so much in control. 'Sorry, would you care to repeat that, please?'

Romy blinked, coming wide awake. At the other end of the phone were staccato tones, familiar tones. Chase had a second phone, one he must keep out of sight. This one in the bedroom which he was speaking into right now—speaking to Mrs Brooks! She sat upright, jamming her shirt back into her jeans.

'For you,' he said coldly, and handed over the receiver.

Her stomach turned to lead.

'Mirabelle Brooks here, Miss MacDonald.' In dismay, Romy watched as Chase grabbed hold of his crutches and levered himself upright. He ignored her frantic pantomime signalling for him to stop, and started to head for the door. 'Sorry to ring in the evening,' Mrs Brooks continued. 'But I've been pestered for months by a client looking for premises where he can set up a small private zoo, and it suddenly clicked that your place would be ideal. The guy's a frustrated animal trainer and——' Romy hardly heard the whys and wherefores, she was too wretched at the sight of Chase limping out of the room, disgust at her betrayal oozing from every pore. 'I guess it's possible the animals could make some noise, but you're so far from anywhere that no one would be disturbed. A few stout cages in that yard of yours would not——'

'Out of the question,' Romy intervened. 'I have a neighbour further up the hill. I couldn't subject him to a zoo!'

'If we twisted my client's arm, I dare say he would be willing to pay a little over the odds. I know how difficult he's finding it to locate a base.'

'No!' Only good manners prevented her from slamming down the phone and rushing after Chase.

'But Miss MacDonald, if you'd allow him to drive out and explain the situation, I'm sure——'

'No, no, *no!* I must go. Thanks for calling.' She abandoned the receiver.

Chase was on the patio, gazing out at an evening sky painted with squiggles of pink and gold and purple. He made a darkly brooding silhouette, aloof in his disdain. Romy shivered, rubbing at her upper arms, though whether her chill came from the breeze blowing off the ocean, or from the knowledge that, in part, she deserved Chase's contempt, she did not determine.

'How could you?' he asked raggedly, turning on her with eyes hard and hurt. 'How could you put your property up for sale, and not tell me? Why wasn't I given the opportunity to buy?'

Romy tired hard to assemble her well thought out arguments. 'It was for your own good.'

'My own good!' he yelled, giving rein to his fury. 'How in the hell is it for my own good for you to deliberately louse up all my plans? Ruin my future?'

'I'm *not* ruining your future,' she protested, trying to believe what she said, though all of a sudden her carefully constructed logic seemed like drivel. 'You're too rigid, too obsessed with having your own way. You must learn to adapt.'

'And you're intending to teach me how to adapt by wrecking all I've striven for? Hell, I've worked damned hard in some Godawful conditions, but the thought that I was earning money to finance the diving ranch kept me going. It gave me impetus. And now you come along, and you, you——' Chase ran out of words, but after a moment started patting his hip.

'What are you doing?' she asked, though she wouldn't have been surprised if he had pulled out a gun and shot her.

'Checking to see I still have my wallet, and maybe I should count my back teeth, too. With you around, nothing's safe,' he sneered.

Guilt washed over her, but the guilt made her angry, angry with Chase and his violent reaction.

'Don't you understand?' Romy demanded with stinging inflection. 'You'd be far happier if you learned to be flexible. Can't you see that you should compromise?'

'No,' he denied, with flat authority.

'You could site your stupid pool elsewhere, I'm sure you could. But you won't.' A treacherous burn of tears came at the back of her eyes. 'And you could fall in love, if you gave yourself half the chance.'

Chase repositioned the crutches. 'With you?'

They looked each other in the eye, simultaneously turning away. Something stirred in Romy, a kind of exasperated malice.

'Don't panic. That programmed life of yours won't be disrupted. I'll soon be gone.'

A slow sardonic smile indicated Chase had a taste for torture. 'Thank goodness. As far as I'm concerned, the sooner I have the bay to myself, the better.'

CHAPTER SEVEN

THERE was no way she could remain beneath his roof. Romy gathered up her possessions and departed, head held high, bravely trying not to care when Chase stayed indoors, this time never bothering to monitor her journey down the hill in the fast-fading light. His lack of consideration was typical. Hadn't she known from the start that the strong-minded Mr O'Donoghue cared only for himself? Only himself. Any attraction he may have felt towards her was no more than the biological response of male to female. Perhaps his sole stimulus in seducing her, or trying to, had been the cabin's acquisition? The idea made a cold shiver run down her spine, yet she was forced to admit to the possibility.

That night Romy lay awake for what seemed to be decades, too preoccupied to care about the obscure creaks and rustles. She went over and over their relationship. Morning came and lack of sleep left her weary and confused, nothing had been solved. Chase did not lend himself to simple descriptions, so her opinion of him continued to see-saw. What tormented most was defining the root cause of his distress the previous evening. True, he had been furious at having his plans disrupted, but hadn't there been more? A hint, a will-o'-the-wisp feeling that what had torn him to shreds had actually been the fact he felt she had betrayed him? In this instance, had Chase allowed his emotions precedence over practicalities?

Hacking down the garden jungle held no attraction, so after breakfast she drifted into odd bits of cleaning and rearranging the lay-out of the living-room. Great-aunt Prudence's furniture was solid, if shabby, and a vigorous application of elbow grease showed dividends. The physical exertion lifted her spirits, and she ventured out to gather wild flowers, arranging them in a surrealistic design, together with shells and pieces of bleached driftwood.

Amidst her activities another worry began to circle—how had Chase coped overnight with his bad ankle? Inherent goodnature prodded Romy to ignore her trepidation and knock on his door, seeking assurance that he was safe and sound, yet her fibrillating heart warned that further contact with the curly-headed Californian would be fatal. But maybe it was too late—wasn't she already a victim of love? When the telephone rang mid-morning and she heard the low purr of his voice, her nerves leapt into a frantic fandango.

'I thought I'd better check that you're okay,' Chase explained tersely, as if *she* was the invalid. Romy decided she was—an emotional one.

With an effort she answered him back in the same tone, for he had spoken like a stranger, strictly formal. 'I'm fine, thank you. How are you?'

'Very well. The ankle is much better.'

To her surprise, he phoned a second time in the evening, and again the following day when she was eating breakfast, though on each occasion he was aloof. Romy readjusted her complaints of his lack of thoughtfulness, yet wondered why he had bothered to phone when ascertaining her well-being appeared to mean no more than an onerous duty.

Needing a change of scene, she decided to drive into San Francisco. Fresh supplies of bread and fruit were required, and maybe time away from the bay would produce a different perspective? She pulled on a loose white voile top and white slacks, and climbed into the car. Now more at ease with the traffic and the routes, Romy gradually relaxed, and by the time she reached the Golden Gate Bridge, she was smiling. Across the blue expanse of water, the skyline of San Francisco glittered in the sunshine, and who could feel miserable gazing at that view? She was a survivor, she decided, and there was no reason why she would not survive her brush with Chase O'Donoghue.

After purchasing her supplies, she became a fully-fledged tourist by walking a block of Lombard Street, reputed to be the 'crookedest street in the world'. The road writhed steeply downhill, like a crazy snake, and she stood to marvel at the cars which braved its hairpin bends. Motoring home in the Buick was tame by comparison, but as Romy headed northwards, leaving the city's excitements behind, so her worries seeped back. She realised that, despite the various spanners she had attempted to toss into the works, Chase had not shifted one inch in his determination to erect a diving ranch on *his* terms. Maybe now, after what he considered her downright treachery, he had decided to retaliate. In all honesty, she could not blame him. And as owner of the land engulfing hers, he was in a strong position to cause trouble.

Romy's mind swung to the shared lane. She had never bothered with the legal jargon when the lawyer had shown her the deeds, but now wished she had. A vague memory surfaced.

Didn't Chase own the actual thoroughfare and
allow her right of way at his discretion? Suppose
he decided to forbid unrestricted approach to her
cabin? Her spirits plummeted as if a kamikaze
pilot had control. Could he do that? No. Yes. No.
Surely he would be legally bound to allow access,
though maybe no vehicular access? But could a
change of ownership nullify any existing arrangement? Suppose he contacted Mrs Brooks and
stated that any future owner of the property
would be denied freedom of the lane?

She started to panic. One minute she was
convincing herself that Chase would never resort
to such a lowdown ruse, but the next she had
decided he would consider all was fair in love and
war, though as far as he was concerned, what
existed between them was most certainly not
love! The way he had interpreted her actions, he
was perfectly entitled to strike back. Romy had
the ghastly sensation of going under for the third
time, with Chase's hand pressing down on her
head for, robbed of vehicular approach, the cabin
would be worthless. The sensible action must be
to cut her losses and accept his offer—if it still
stood! Chase was no fool. He could easily
manoeuvre her into a position where she would
have no option but to accept any figure he
offered, even if it was peanuts. The lane was one
way of backing her into a corner, yet doubtless
there were others. Her electricity and water
supplies must cross his land, did he control them
too? The machinations seemed tremendous.

By the time she parked the Buick alongside the
freshly-painted fence, Romy was resigned to her
miserable defeat. For a long moment she stood
and gazed at the cabin's white glossed walls, and

then went indoors. The smell of cats had disappeared long ago. Now the rooms were spanking clean, glowing freshly with the care and attention she had lavished over the past weeks, and her heart began to bleed. All her work, her hopes, the enthusiasm, all her devotion, counted for nothing because she knew that the minute Chase took possession the cabin would be bulldozed from the face of the earth.

She forced herself to lift up the phone and dial his number, desperate to renounce her claim and settle the matter once and for all. With gritted teeth, she listened as the call went unanswered. Valiantly Romy tried again twenty minutes later, and twenty minutes after that, in case he was in the shower or hot tub, but there was no reply. Chase's joke about falling down and expiring flashed into her head, but he had sounded so much in control when he had rung earlier that she decided it was far more likely he had sneaked out for a clandestine jog.

There was no alternative but to abandon her quest, and when a pang of hunger reminded her it was early afternoon, she decided to make some lunch. Romy sliced hefty chunks of French bread and began to prepare an open sandwich. She was involved in layering crispy lettuce with tomato, boiled egg and roll mop herring, when there was a knock at the front door. Licking mayonnaise from her fingers, she went to open it and discovered Mrs Brooks stood to attention on the verandah.

'Good afternoon,' mumbled Romy, thumb in mouth.

The woman smiled. 'Sorry to call unannounced, but I couldn't reach you earlier because your line was engaged, so I took a chançe.' She half-turned to indicate a man behind her. 'May I introduce Mr O'Donoghue?'

Romy's eyes grew round as pennies for, beyond the woman's shoulder, she now saw Chase carefully negotiating the steps on his crutches. The dishevelled invalid had gone; he was trim in a lemon sports shirt and beige slacks. The sight of him made her clench her fists, mindless of the remnants of mayonnaise. So Chase and Mrs Brooks had joined forces! He must have explained his stranglehold to the agent and brought her along to advise Romy that she would be wise to grab whatever pittance he chose to offer, and be thankful. Two against one, she thought grimly. She was about to blurt out not to bother with ulti-matums, that she relinquished her claim and Chase could have the damned property—in Christmas wrapping, for all she cared—when Mrs Brooks spoke again.

'Mr O'Donoghue is from out of of town and he's interested in your house.'

Out of town? Romy thought. She threw him a suspicious glance, but he merely nodded and held out a formal hand.

'Er, my fingers are gummed up,' Romy explained, needing to avoid contact. She sucked her thumb like mad, wondering what on earth Chase was up to. 'Do come inside,' she said, when Mrs Brooks gave a little cough to indicate some movement was expected.

As soon as they entered the living-room, the real estate agent launched into her sales pitch, stressing how the outside of the building had been freshly painted and that the inside was 'real quaint'. When Chase looked impressed and murmured compliments, Romy began to boil.

'I can tell you've been working hard, Miss MacDonald,' he said, nodding his approval.

'Yes, I have.' Her tone prickled. Now she had worked out the reason for his visit—he must have come to gloat! They both knew the cabin's condition counted for nothing. What difference did it make if the scrubbed floors gleamed pale gold beneath the slanting rays of the sun, or that the kitchen cupboards had been coaxed into sweet-smelling perfection, when at the first opportunity he would destroy—destroy—destroy! Okay, she was not fighting any longer, Chase had won, but he did not have to act out this cruel scene, with her and Mrs Brooks as bit players. 'But it's not the building which interests you is it, Mr O'Donoghue? It's the land,' she snapped.

He looked unperturbed. 'Both,' he said.

'Beautiful situation, so peaceful,' Mrs Brooks intervened. 'And you have your own private bathing beach. Neat, huh?'

Romy treated Chase to a poisonous smile. 'The place is falling apart. If you've travelled, I'm sure you'll have seen better ghettos in Calcutta.'

'Indonesia,' he corrected.

Mrs Brooks cleared her throat, sensing that the conversation was slewing off in an odd direction. 'Splendid opportunities to study the flora and fauna,' she put in heartily.

Romy was concentrating on Chase. If he could play games, so could she, though nothing made much sense any more. 'You wouldn't be happy here,' she said. 'Los Angeles would suit a man like you. They have blondes in bikinis there, and——'

'Group sex?' he added helpfully.

'Shall we take a look at the outside of the property?' Mrs Brooks gabbled. 'It shows great potential.'

Following the house agent as she led the way outdoors, Romy was possessed with a desperate urge to push the sadistic Mr O'Donogue down the verandah steps, crutches and all. He deserved to be punished, for he was juggling the cabin around like a pile of plates spinning atop a wand, plates which, at any moment, he would take great delight in allowing to crash to the ground.

'Well-painted fence,' he commented.

'Sure is,' Mrs Brooks enthused. 'And there's so much space out here. A keen gardener could transform this yard into a showpiece.' Her enthusiasm changed the entire skimble-skamble of tangled foliage into the lawns and fountains of Versailles.

Romy's eyes glittered like the glare on the ocean. 'And if gardening isn't your scene, you could always dig a great big hole and have a swimming pool. In fact, why not knock down my house and have an *Olympic* sized pool, plus saunas and massage parlours,' she said recklessly. 'Wouldn't that be fun?'

He raised his brows at 'massage parlours' and shifted on his crutches. 'But why would I do that? The guy up the hill is planning a pool on the far side of the lane. I dare say he'd allow me to swim there.'

'A pool on the far side of the lane?' she questioned tartly.

Mrs Brooks had given up trying to organise the conversation and was content to be a bystander as she figured out what was happening.

Chase nodded. 'The land across there is a touch uneven, but a couple of days with earthmoving gear should soon sort that out.'

'But the pool's planned for *here*!' retorted Romy, a flourish of her arms outlining the perimeter of her garden. He shrugged. 'I guess the guy up the hill must have changed his mind.'

Romy sucked at her mayonnaise tainted fingers, not knowing what to say next. Was this an about-face, or some diabolical form of revenge?

'Wonderful sea views,' Mrs Brooks said brightly, getting her second wind.

'Miss MacDonald and I have things to discuss, so maybe you'd like to drive back to your office?' Chase suggested politely. 'I'll be in touch later.'

'You want me to leave you *here*?' the woman asked, as though he had suggested being parachuted into Outer Mongolia.

'Yes please.'

'But how will you get back to 'Frisco?'

'I'll handle it.'

She clutched her clipboard. 'Well, if you're sure?'

'I'm sure,' he confirmed, with a dazzling smile.

Lost for words, Mrs Brooks climbed into her car and motored off up the hill.

Romy rubbed her nose in puzzlement. 'I don't understand. Did you go all the way into San Francisco earlier on, just so she could bring you out here?'

'No. I met her further back along the track. I'd concocted a tale of how a friend had dropped me off there.'

'But why all the play-acting?' The implication of Chase building the pool on *his* land was sinking in, but Romy needed time to work through the implications.

'I was a bit chicken about approaching you,' he confessed. 'So I reckoned that Mrs Brooks would be protection. At least with her in tow, you weren't likely to fling paint all over me, or slam the door in my face.'

'Point taken, but why did——?'

Chase interrupted her. 'Do you mind if we go back inside? I'd like to sit down. All this hopping around gets to be pretty tiring.'

When she agreed, and he limped up the steps and into the living-room, Romy noticed fine lines of strain around his eyes. He was not quite as fit as she had first supposed.

'You're still supposed to be horizontal,' she chided. 'For someone who always does things properly, you're not making much headway with the doctor's instructions.' He pulled a face and slumped heavily on to the old sofa. Suddenly Romy remembered she had still not eaten lunch. 'I've just made a sandwich, but there's enough for two. Will you join me?'

He nodded. 'Sounds great.'

She was quickly back, placing a napkin across his knee, setting out the open sandwich and cups of steaming coffee on the carved chest which did duty as an occasional table.

'Let me get this straight,' she said, sitting down beside him. 'You don't want to knock down my house?'

'No, not any longer.' Food intervened, for Chase appeared to be as hungry as she was, and together they ate in silence. 'I really like this,' he said, taking another bite. At last he was able to speak. 'I've been doing some serious thinking and you're right, I can site the pool and health club facilities elsewhere. I guess because I've had things planned for years I was too pigheaded to accept that there could be alternatives.' He raised his hand to lick a smear of mayonnaise from his hair-sprinkled wrist. 'Hell, this stuff gets everywhere. Why is it I always seem to get coated when I'm with you, if not in paint, in salad dressing?'

Romy was beginning to feel happy. 'Don't complain,' she chastised with a grin. 'The protein is good for your skin. I read in a health magazine once that if you want to stay young, you should rub yourself all over with mayonnaise and then rush out and roll in the snow.'

Chase pulled down his mouth. 'Sounds like a recipe for cardiac arrest to me!'

She felt impelled to return to important matters. 'So does this mean you're no longer interested in acquiring my property?'

'Definitely not. You must stay in the bay and——'

'No, no,' she interrupted, slicing a hand through the air in a positive denunciation. 'I don't want the cabin, you can have it. I accept your offer, if it still stands.' Romy's hidden fears began to spill out incoherently. 'I know because you control the lane you can state your own price ... I'm willing to abide by that ... the legacy came out of the blue anyway ... I'm not interested in making a vast profit ... I was wrong to interfere with your plans ... I should never have tried to sell the cabin to anyone but you ... the verbal agreement makes it morally yours, and I had some foolish idea of ... oh, I don't know.' Her hands were tick-tacking in mid-air. 'I imagined I was acting from the best motives, but now I see that I was wrong.'

Chase put his hand on her wrist and squeezed gently. 'Ease up. You weren't wrong, it was me. I had tunnel vision about having the diving ranch built exactly as first specified, and I guess this obsession with my own ideas made me refuse to admit to other options. But what's all this talk about the lane, where does that fit in?' He listened, sipping his coffee, as Romy described her wild imaginings. 'What kind of a guy do you think I am?' he demanded when she had finished, and she saw from the hardening of his jaw that she had offended him. 'I would never isolate the cabin like that, even if I could. I know I have a quick temper and can be bloody-minded at times, but I'd never force anyone into submission by pulling a dirty trick like that. Let's face it, if I had been merciless I could have squeezed Prudence MacDonald out of here years ago.'

'You could—how?' Romy asked in surprise.

'For a start, by taking her to court over Alex's agreement that the property would be sold when he died.'

'But because that was only verbal, you would never have won,' she retorted.

'I agree, though for years Alex had spoken of selling the cabin to Paddy, and in front of witnesses. No, having Prudence's lifestyle brought into the public eye is what would have helped me. Anyone would have seen straight away that it was dangerous for the old gal to live in a lone wooden shack.' He broke off for a mouthful of coffee. 'You're young and strong, you can cope, but Prudence was old. She had great difficulty climbing the hill, and because she

couldn't drive, she was trapped. The telephone
was her only contact with the outside world and,
even then, she was at a disadvantage because her
mind wandered half the time. Only visits from
Mrs Klein, bringing supplies from the supermarket, kept her going, visits which Mrs Klein
resented. For years she had been trying to have
her sister move nearer to Oakland, though not too
near!' he added drily. 'You can bet that if
Prudence had appeared in court with her matted
white hair and mumble-jumbles, the judge or the
Welfare would have been duty bound to remove
her to a protected environment. And the money I
was willing to pay for the property would have
ensured she could have lived in comfort for the
remainder of her days.' He took another gulp of
coffee. 'And there were always the cats.'

'What about the cats?' Romy asked sus-
piciously.

'I've never delved into State law, but there has
to be legislation prohibiting senile old women
from giving house-room to more than a dozen
half-wild animals. On smell alone I could have
nailed her for my citizen's loss of fresh air!'

'But getting rid of the cats wouldn't have
meant getting rid of Prudence.'

'Wrong, kiddo. They represented her children,
her family, all that was important in life. She was
in love with the damn things, used to walk
around with them in her arms. You can be sure
that if the cats had been taken away, she would
have died from a broken heart.'

Romy assimilated what he had said. 'So, in
actual fact, you were Mr Kindness personified?'
she scoffed, not knowing whether to be disdainful
or admiring.

'Fat chance! But events could have been manipulated, if I'd had the inclination.' He frowned down at his bandaged ankle and winced. 'Would you mind if we go up to my place and finish off this conversation in my hot tub? The muscle's still sore, and a spell in warm water works wonders.'

A flush came unbidden to her cheeks. Romy knew fine what would happen if she and Chase climbed into that hot tub together. 'You go on alone,' she said, giving a light laugh to deny her alarm. 'There's nothing more to discuss. I'd be grateful if you would buy the cabin because I'm moving out as soon as possible. I'll need time to dispose of the contents, but tomorrow I'll contact an auction room and ask if they'll take the job lot.' Her voice trailed off for Chase had stiffened. He was leaning towards her, shoulders tense, his eyes a stormy blue as he tried hard to bottle his thunder, but it proved impossible.

'What the hell are you talking about?' he exploded. 'Don't you understand? You're staying on. I'll help finish off clearing your yard and then I'll repair the roof.'

Romy's chin jutted. 'I'm leaving the bay.'

'No, you're not!'

'Yes, I am.'

Sensing that they were in danger of having a slanging match, Chase made himself calm down. 'But we've settled everything, so why in the hell quit now?'

'For a variety of reasons,' she stalled and wafted her hands. The only true reason was that she was terrified of becoming trapped in a relationship with him. Romy knew that if they lived at close quarters, a deeper involvement was inevitable and though she was a survivor, she had her limits. 'The bay is too quiet,' she said, seeing he expected a solid excuse.

'But it won't be quiet once the diving ranch is functioning. Look,' he said earnestly, with an air of getting down to brass tacks. 'I intend to work one more stint abroad, and then I'll be based here permanently. Together we——'

'You don't need me,' she put in, thinking that 'permanently' meant he would be permanently holding her heart, permanently willing for her to have the physical man, but never the emotional one. Romy swallowed hard. 'And you don't need the cabin sitting right in the middle of all your splendid arrangements. Pull it down and revert to your original ideas.'

Her reference to the cabin went unnoticed. 'Of course I need you, Romy. Setting up the ranch on my own won't be any fun.' Chase frowned, as though the words had taken him by surprise, then he continued rapidly, 'Come on up to the house and let me show you the plans. I'd like to know what you think. I'm open to fresh angles.' He made a grab for his crutches and hauled himself to his feet. 'Come along.'

'Let's leave it for now,' she protested, as he thumped and swung towards the door at a brisk pace. 'You're tired. I can look at the diagrams another day.'

Chase swivelled back. 'No, I'm fine now. Those sandwiches revived me.' Perhaps they had, or maybe it was his enthusiasm which had given him a new lease of life, but in this mood he was not to be deterred, and, against her better judgment, Romy found herself being talked out of the cabin and up the hill. 'When you see the full extent of the development, you'll realise how exciting it's going to be.' He managed to pause in his spiel when they reached the lounge. Chase made directly for a roll-top desk. 'There,' he said, indicating half a dozen cardboard tubes packed with rolls of white paper. 'Could you carry these? I daren't go into the hot tub with them, but maybe if I stretch out on the bed my ankle will stop throbbing.'

'Can't you stretch out on the sofa?' she suggested, arms piled high with the tubes Chase had given her, but she was too late. He was thumping and swinging towards his bedroom like an athletic peg leg Pete. Romy followed, wondering why she had let him coerce her into coming here. She was all kinds of a fool. Being with Chase on his home ground was fatal. Hadn't the past taught her how susceptible she was to him and those clear blue eyes? Oh, what she would have given for a wet paintbrush right now!

He sat down on the bed, positioned a pillow against the padded head-board and swivelled to stretch out his long legs on top of the covers. 'Come here and take a look,' he said, patting the space beside him.'

There was no option but to do as she was told. Chase carefully slid the rolls of paper from the tubes and opened out sketch plans, detailed drawings, front, side and back elevations of a wide range of buildings. His enthusiasm was infectious and, as she studied the drawings and listened to him, she almost found herself wishing she would be around to see his dreams reach fruition.

'It's intoxicating stuff,' she agreed.

An artist's impression showed how the natural

contours of the land would be skilfully employed
to allow the guest cottages complete privacy, yet
access to all the amenities. Most of the trees
would be retained, and grassy stretches between
the buildings indicated that the ranch promised
to blend in with the surrounding countryside.

'Timber and natural stone is being utilised,' he
explained. 'An architect friend did an up-date last
year, so apart from alterations to siting the pool
and health club facilities, the general plan is
much as shown here.' He smiled at the drawings,
and then up at her. 'The ranch will be great,
Romy. You'll love it.'

I'll love *you*, she wailed inwardly, trying to
swallow down a lump which had unexpectedly
formed in her throat. How wonderful everything
could be if, if . . .

'You'll have a tremendous future. The ranch
looks tremendous,' she assured him. 'But as I
said before, I won't be around. I've changed my
mind about settling in California. Remember me,
the capricious oddball in the silver suit?' She
tried for the flamboyant gesture, but her hands
faltered. 'I'm the square root of useless.'

'Don't say that!' Chase roughly pushed the
plans aside and slid an arm around her shoulders.
'I was wrong. You're steady and reliable. The
way you tackled the painting of the cabin was
incredible, day-in, day-out, coat after coat. I'm
full of admiration.'

'You never said so at the time,' she rebuked.

Chase groped for an answer. 'I guess I found it
hard to admit to being impressed by a—a girl!'

'How would you like me to grab a hold of your
ankle and twist your foot anti-clockwise very,
very slowly?' demanded Romy, mock-angrily.

'That has to be the most chauvinistic remark in years, and *I* thought Californians were liberated! You must be a throwback to the caveman era.'

His lips brushed her temple. 'With your encouragement, I'm prepared to have a shot at making it back to the twentieth century.'

She pulled back. 'Sorry, but once the cabin has been cleared, I shall be on the first flight out.'

His arm captured her again. 'For heaven's sakes, Romy, see sense. Look, you nailed me and made me face up to the fact that I was inflexible, too concerned with having my own way, but that's all changed.' His fingers began to move in a slow sensuous path up and down her arm. 'You've done so much in the way of improvements to the cabin, you can't turn your back on everything now. I've worked out a scheme for incorporating it into the ranch. Wouldn't you like to hear my ideas?'

'No.' Curiosity got the better of her. 'Yes.'

'I'm suggesting the cabin is used as a small café and common meeting ground. Self-catering facilities are to be provided in the guest cabins, but I'm sure people would be glad of a comfortable place where they could have a coffee, or a pizza and salad. The place *is* quaint, like Mrs Brooks said, and has far more charm than some bland modern snackbar.'

'How about providing Devonshire cream teas?' she suggested, carried away for the moment. 'I was intending to make macrame pot holders and hang flowering plants all around the verandah. And position a rocking chair where you could sit and watch the ocean.'

Chase saw his chance and leapt. 'So why not stay and turn those ideas into reality? I plan to run courses for nine months of the year, and use the winter period for maintenance work, then take a break. Join me, Romy,' he suggested. 'If you did find life lonely, though I doubt you would,' he added quickly, 'you could always take time off to visit your father, or he could come and stay here with us.'

'With us?'

She suspected the 'us' meant far more than her living in the cabin and Chase up on the hill. They seemed to have travelled a long way in a short time.

'If we turn your place into an eating house there won't be room for you, will there?' he asked reasonably. 'So you'll move in with me. This place is more than big enough for two. Okay, so occasionally you might spill something all over me, but I have no doubt there'll be compensations.'

The gleam in his eye told her exactly what compensations he had in mind. Romy held barricading hands in the air as he leaned closer. 'Hold it right there!' Her heart was banging wildly. 'You appear to have this scheme mapped out to the nth degree, but as usual it satisfies one person—you!'

'I'd make very sure that you'd be satisfied too,' he said, his eyes wandering over her face to settle on her lips.

'But I happen to have my own plans for the future,' Romy announced, though, in truth, she rarely planned further ahead than the next meal, if that. 'I shall return to England, marry Peter and—and move to Bangkok.'

His arm fell from her. 'And who in hell's name happens to be Peter?' he rasped.

Having produced the young man with the air of a magician producing a rabbit from a top hat, Romy was trapped. Too late she remembered that, in his last note, Peter had agreed that their break had been for the best, saying that as a bachelor he could devote more attention to climbing the diplomatic ladder. 'Have small talk, will travel,' she had thought wryly at the time.

'Peter is a friend, a good friend.'

'And you're prepared to marry a *friend*?' he asked in disbelief.

Romy leapt off the bed. 'Well, yes. Why not?'

'I'll tell you why not,' he said, hauling himself on to his crutches and hopping round to confront her. 'Because you belong here, with *me*!'

He reached for her, trying to control the crutches beneath his armpits and keep his balance at the same time. Romy half-turned, intent on escape, but Chase grabbed for her again and together they toppled on to the bed, the crutches bouncing around them.

'Your ankle!' she gasped, breathless from the sudden weight of him on top of her.

'To hell with my ankle,' he murmured, pleased with the way things had turned out. He burrowed his hands into the red richness of her hair, holding her captive. 'Baby, please don't leave,' he whispered, kissing the warm fragrant column of her throat. She struggled, and he shifted to lie beside her, careful to keep one leg pinning her down. '*Please*. I've never wanted a woman so much in all my life. You haunt me, the lilt of your voice is always in my ears, and when you look at me with those big green eyes...' His voice faded and he sighed, nuzzling his face into her shoulder. 'You're driving me wild, Romy. I want to feel you around me like a sea anenome, opening and closing, holding me inside you.'

His words made a sweet aching warmth spread deep within her, and she twisted restlessly but his leg imprisoned her more tightly, pressing into her thighs, making her devastatingly aware of the desire which was building between them. Romy felt dizzy. All she wanted to do was return the kisses which were moving inexorably to the upward swell of her breasts.

'Move in with me, baby,' he implored, his mouth a hot harbinger of the joys to come.

'No,' she moaned, summoning up the tatters of her self-control. With a superhuman effort, Romy managed to slide out from beneath him and push herself upright. 'Chase, this is all wrong,' she told him, backing towards the door.

'Why?' He sat up on the edge of the bed, running a hand through his rumpled hair. 'Live with me and let's see how things turn out.'

'I can't.' Her voice was strained. 'It would be a mistake. I couldn't, I——' She took a deep breath. 'I'm not someone like Julia.'

'You want a wedding ring?' he accused flatly.

'Oh God, I knew you'd say that,' she wailed in despair. 'Okay, yes. Yes, I do want a wedding ring, but most of all I want *love*.' She paused, clinging on to the door for support. 'And I don't see why I should have to apologise or justify my feelings to a cynical bastard like you. The whole social structure is based on marriage and families. I believe in commitment, Chase, and to me commitment means giving, with nothing held back, no escape route. I'm not interested in holding something in reserve, in case things don't go right. I know you can argue that a marriage certificate is just a piece of paper, but isn't it also a demonstration that you love someone enough to devote your life to them?'

'Ha, and how many of these lovely marriages of yours end in divorce?' he barked.

Romy flung a hand. 'I know, I know, but hopefully they all begin with the best intentions. Starting off as a live-in lover, or a live-out lover for that matter, comes nowhere in my book. I'm perfectly aware that plenty of couples co-habit satisfactorily, never needing a marriage ceremony and, fine, that works for them. But it wouldn't work for me. I'm a one-man woman, Chase. I'm not the type who packs her cosmetics and moves on. I need to know I can afford to give all—and take all—and be secure.'

'Do you imagine I'd throw you out in the cold?' he asked, sounding hurt.

'No, it's not that. I'm not talking about security of board and lodgings, or money. It's emotional security that matters to me.' She sighed. 'You and I would fight like hell at times, Chase. You have a hot temper and, let's face it, domesticity is not my strong suit. I have a tendency to leave long hairs in the bath, and I don't keep my records in alphabetical order.'

He glowered at her. 'That's below the belt. So, we'd have rows, but we'd make them up.'

'Would we? Isn't the solution when the going gets tough and you're only living together, to call it a day? Spilt milk and no harm done?' She gave a sour little laugh. 'But my guts would be lying there on the floor, my *heart*! When I give, I'm going to give all of me. Tawdry little affairs with a get-out clause are not my style.'

Blue eyes narrowed, Chase studied her. 'Tell

me something,' he said slowly. 'Are you a virgin?'

Romy met his gaze. 'Yes.'

'Oh hell!'

'Virgins are supposed to be prized, not treated like oddities,' she retorted, trying to sound flip and cool, when inside she was dying.

Chase glared, definitely not amused. 'But I imagined that you'd—you'd been around. You're beautiful, you're modern. Most girls of your age don't think twice about——' He cut the sentence off stone dead and took a shuddering breath. 'Okay, I'll buy the cabin at my original price. I'll also take over the contents, so if you'll tot up how much the whole collection's worth I'll give you cash. I'll ask Stu to set the necessary paperwork in motion.' He knotted his hands between his knees and slumped forward. 'You'd better go now. I feel exhausted.'

CHAPTER EIGHT

NEXT morning, Romy had phoned Chase to say he could have the cabin's contents, free of charge.

'What you're paying for the property suits me fine. The proceeds are pennies from heaven, anyway, thanks to Prudence, so I'd be grateful if you would accept the entire package as it stands.'

Chase had been indignant. 'There's no way I'm prepared to have a houseful of furniture as a free gift. I insist on paying the going rate.'

'But there's nothing of much value,' she had protested..

'The furniture has to be worth something!'

His outrage warned she had better come up with a figure substantial enough to satisfy him, but that was easier said than done. Romy did not have a clue as to the worth of her great-aunt's possessions. For a while she toyed with bringing in an independent valuer, but eventually abandoned the idea. Although Prudence's belongings were old, they were a long way off antique, falling instead into a no-man's-land where scrap value would be the most she could expect to realise. Probably an expert would quote a figure and submit a bill of seventy per cent of that to cover his services, and whilst she had no desire to make extra from Chase, wasting money was foolish. But choosing a middle-of-the-road sum which would meet his approval was a difficult task, Romy was relieved when her father telephoned, and she could ask his advice.

'I warned you'd soon be packing your suitcases again,' he chortled, taking at face value her comment about the bay not being the haven she had first expected.

Romy let that ride. 'But first I have to cost the furniture,' she explained. 'How much should I ask for a mahogany bedroom suite, comprising a double bed, wardrobe and chest of drawers?'

'Coming up with a valuation, sight unseen, isn't very ethical,' he pointed out.

'Pa, all I need is a rough estimate,' she pleaded.

'Fair enough, but it will be very rough.' Romy began to describe the furniture while her father hazarded guesses, and eventually the larger items were price-tagged. The smaller pieces she would deal with herself. 'Peter will be sorry he's missed your return,' her father remarked, when they had time for gossip. 'He left for Bangkok last night. He should go down well out there, he's such an amusing fellow. Tells some marvellous tales.'

Yes, she thought as she replaced the receiver, but there's more to life than being a whizz at repartee, or keeping your long-playing records in alphabetical order!

An inventory was compiled. Taking one room at a time, Romy followed a methodical route, determined to show Chase how professional she could be—a final reminder that she was not at all the scatterbrained kook of his original assessment. A nominal sum was neatly marked against each item. How thankful she was that the drawers and cupboards had been the first to receive her attention, for what now lay on the scented lining paper was clean and respectable.

Among the paraphernalia were a few treasures, such as a pretty procelain pomander, and

she listed these separately with a view to having
them air-freighted home. *Home*, Romy thought
miserably, where's my home now? With a
conscious effort, she refused to brood and carried
on. When a value was totally beyond her, she left
blanks with the vague notion that Chase might
help, though he was in no mood to become
involved. All he required was a round figure in
order that he could fork out the cash and wave a
hasty goodbye.

The following day her list was complete, and
she telephoned to ask if he could spare her some
time.

'One or two matters need discussing,' she
explained.

Chase was stiff and starchy. 'All I need is the
final amount,' he protested.

His determination to avoid her was irritating.
'I can guarantee it won't be fatal if you happen to
breathe in the same air space as me,' she replied
tartly.

He started to speak in protest, then changed his
mind. 'I'll be down,' he agreed, and was knocking
at the front door within minutes.

Dressed in a black sports shirt and denims,
Chase was back to being the Greek god
advertisement again, yet there was a cautious look
in his eyes, and his whole attitude shouted a
silent 'hands off' message. Romy tried her best to
understand how he felt and why, but it was an
artificial best. If he was incapable of coping with
a woman who happened to believe that love and
sex and marriage were irretrievably combined,
that was his problem.

'How's the ankle?' she enquired, as he strode
into the living-room.

His response was stilted. 'Fine, thank you. I've finished with the crutches, so hopefully I should be jogging again come weekend.'

'You'll be safe because I won't be around in the Buick,' said Romy, trying for a joke, but failing miserably.

'You're not leaving so soon?' he demanded.

'In four days' time.'

Chase strode over to the window, standing with his back to her, one hand in his trouser pocket as he gazed out at the ocean. It was late afternoon, a time when the air seemed gin-clear, making the colours of sky, sea and earth vivid and vital. Little white topped waves ran up the sand like excited children, and ran back down again.

'Why hurry away?' he asked. 'The good weather is forecast to continue, and you must admit that the bay's a pretty fantastic place to be in the sunshine.'

'The bay's lovely,' she agreed, a throb in her voice.

'So why not remain here a while?' He half-turned and she saw that the dead look had left his eyes and he was enthusiastic. 'Why don't I teach you how to snorkel? We could buy a wetsuit and——' He stopped talking and turned back to the window. 'Who am I kidding? It wouldn't work,' he muttered. When he faced her again, he was formal. 'What are you planning to do during your last four days?'

'Tomorrow I'm having a last attempt at clearing the garden. I know I don't have a cat in hell's chance of making much progress, but I'd like to leave everything reasonably tidy.'

His voice was gruff. 'Don't bother. I'll tackle the undergrowth when you've gone.'

'Right now the garden belongs to me, so I'll do what I want!' she said, her green eyes taking on a stubborn glint.

His broad shoulders moved. 'Okay, and after tomorrow?'

'Once details are settled with Mrs Brooks and my lawyer, I'm hitting the tourist trail. Not taking a look around San Francisco while I have the chance, would be a sin.'

'Eat seafood at Fisherman's Wharf and sail around Alcatraz,' he suggested. 'If you're looking for souvenirs, Ghirardelli Square is a great shopping area.'

Romy could not help noticing how he deliberately made no offer to go with her. But why should he? All Chase wanted from her was sex, companionship was as little use to him as love. She waved a hand towards the dining table where her papers were stacked. 'Can I show you my inventory?'

Chase pulled up a chair and scanned the handwritten sheets.

'That's fine,' he announced, seconds later.

'No, it's not,' she protested. 'You might as well have been reading Arabic for all the sense you made.'

'It's fine,' he repeated, a steel thread running through his voice.

'Even the blanks?'

'What blanks?'

Romy shook an admonishing finger. 'See, you weren't reading the inventory. I might be cheating you rotten for all you know, and to be fair to the both of us, I'd be grateful if you would check my additions. I'm not too hot on arithmetic.' Earnestly she began pointing out the sub-totals and where she had carried them forward.

'How come you're so painstaking all of a sudden?' Chase accused, sitting stiffly beside her.

'Looks like somebody has to be!'

A muscle leapt in his cheek. 'I don't see why. Just tell me how much cash you need to keep you happy, and I'll provide it.'

'That's not the point.' Romy felt a spurt of anger. 'You're supposed to be the guy who crosses all the t's and dots all the i's, so get cracking.' She thrust the sheaf of papers in front of him.

Chase ignored them. 'You mentioned a friend of yours called Peter. Just how serious are things between you two?'

Bemused by the sudden switch in conversation, Romy did not bother with pretence. 'Things aren't serious at all. He asked me to marry him, but——' Her arm lifted into a ballerina movement. 'But he's another character like my father, all bonhomie, a piece of social flotsam. Peter would hate to put down roots.'

'And that's why you refused him?'

'No. I refused him because I didn't love him.'

Chase digested that, his blue eyes thoughtful, then returned to his interrogation. 'What will you do back in London?'

'Find myself a job. Believe it or not, I make quite an efficient secretary,' she thrust back, giving way to a touch of rebellion.

'I do believe you.' He turned his attention to the papers. 'What is it you want me to do?'

Romy was brisk. 'First, I'll show you the items I couldn't price and we can fix a sum, then maybe you'd better check on the values I've marked down and see if they're satisfactory, then——'

'I'm not doing all that,' he interrupted, leafing impatiently through the pages. He came to the final temporary total. 'Can I make a suggestion? I'll give you this——' He tapped an index finger on the bottom line. '—Plus a thousand dollars. Is that okay?'

'No, it's not!' squeaked Romy.

'Two thousand?' Chase sounded exhausted, willing to agree to anything in order to finalise the matter.

'Two *hundred* will be more than enough.'

'Only two hundred, are you sure?' He ran a weary hand through his hair, careless of the way he was mussing up the curls. 'Look, this is not a great day for me to be talking finance. Let's settle on five hundred.'

'No, two!' In exasperation Romy pushed up the sleeves of her bronze sweatshirt, worn with slacks of the same shade. 'I hope you don't intend to run that diving ranch of yours in this slaphappy fashion,' she rebuked. 'You'll be bankrupt before you start.'

He locked his eyes with hers, and then looked away. 'Can I be honest? I'm not at all convinced I want to develop the damn ranch after all.'

'Of course you do!'

Chase rose to his feet and began pacing restlessly across the pine-planked floor. 'I don't know what the hell's the matter with me. For years the lousy ranch has meant so much, but now that finally it's within reach I don't know if it's what I want any more.' He stopped in his pacing to frown at her. 'I guess maybe this erratic state of mind means I could be suffering from the male menopause.'

Romy hooted with laughter, her tension dissolving in her rocking merriment. For all the world Chase reminded her of a troubled lion, prowling back and forth, weighed down with his troubles.

'Oh, Chase!' she giggled.

He refused to admit to any humour. 'It's not funny. I just know I'm in big trouble here.'

'Never. The ranch'll be fine. You're a bit intense this morning, that's all,' she said encouragingly, trying to pull her features into a solemn state. 'Your mood will pass.'

He studied his black moccasins. 'Will it?' he asked morosely. 'Right now I feel like ripping those goddamn plans to shreds.' He gave a dry grunt. 'Though my father would be sure to come back and haunt me night and day if I did.' For the first time a smile tugged at the corner of his mouth. 'And Paddy would make one heck of a ghost, believe you me.'

'He'd be hard going?'

'Yeah, and he *was* hard going.' Chase lounged back into the chair beside her. 'He'd be sure to blame my change of mind on my mother. Whenever I did something to annoy him, Paddy would blame it on her, poor woman. He reckoned my hot temper came from her side of the family.' A memory lit up his smile again. 'My one saving grace was that I don't throw things. According to Paddy when they quarrelled, my mother would chuck anything which came to hand. That drove him wild! He'd be spreadeagled, desperate to protect the walls and the carpets, and my mother would be flinging cups and plant pots right, left and centre.'

'Sounds dangerous,' Romy grinned.

'Sounds hilarious, but he could never see it like that. Paddy had a healthy sense of humour about most things, but never about life with my mother.'

Romy rested her chin on her hands and looked at him. 'How long were they married?'

'Three years. Three years of hell, according to Paddy. Why they joined forces in the first place, I'll never know. They must have been totally incompatible.'

'But even if they were opposites, everything would have worked out all right if they'd loved each other?' Romy suggested.

'Maybe,' he admitted. 'But my father was too involved in keeping his own private world in order to put much value on love. Affection he could manage, but love?' He shrugged.

'And what was your mother like?'

'I was only a little guy of two when she went out of my life, so I don't remember anything personally, but from all accounts she was impetuous, emotional, passionate. Paddy must have driven her into a frenzy with his fetish for routine, and the older he became, the worse he was. Talk about hypercritical! Everything had to be done properly, and either you shaped up, or you shipped out. My mother shipped out!'

'But you shaped up?'

'I had no choice. Don't forget that as a child Paddy's ways were the only ways I knew, so for years I took it for granted that everyone was a hygiene fanatic. I remember how shocked I was when I first realised that not everyone in the world rinsed out the dish towel after each use! I've often wondered whether the final straw for my mother came over an unrinsed dish towel,' he chuckled. 'Equally, it could have been a button she neglected to sew on, or a dripping shower. There wasn't much that escaped Paddy's eagle eye and then he used to grumble like crazy.'

Romy's brow creased. 'Why didn't your mother take you with her when she left?'

'She did, initially. The pair of us moved in with my grandmother. She had a huge house in a busy neighbourhood. She ran it like a community hall. There were aunts and uncles buzzing around, and neighbours by the million in for a gossip or a cup of coffee. There was a great deal of talking, hugging and kissing, so life was one heck of a contrast to Paddy's decorous ways. To support us, my mother found herself a job and I was left to the mercies of whoever was around at the time. I have a cousin who's four or five years older and she used to play with me, feed me candy, cart me all over the place like some kind of doll.' He grinned, leaning back in his chair. 'The story goes that Paddy arrived one afternoon, immaculately neat and tidy, face scrubbed, hair combed, all set to take me out. At first they couldn't find me, but eventually I wandered in with a runny nose and filthy knees, and he nearly went crazy. He ranted and raved, said my mother wasn't fit to bring up a child and that I'd end up with cholera. There was another almighty fight.'

'More airborne plant pots?'

'You bet. The outcome was that Paddy took me off. My grandmother says my mother agreed, thinking that a spell of caring for a two-year old would teach him a few of the messier facts of life, and that as far as she was concerned it was a temporary arrangement.'

'But it wasn't?'

'No. A couple of weeks later my mother was knocked down and killed by a hit-and-run driver.'

'So you remained with your father?' Romy asked.

He nodded. 'Until I started school he employed a housekeeper, though he spent as much time with me as he could. Despite being a hard taskmaster, he was good with kids. So long as I went his way, things were fine. He wasn't one of those fathers who sit and snore in front of the television all weekend, far from it! We'd go fishing and camping. He taught me the value of organisation, that I should always be in control of myself. Mind you, at times he was murder. As I grew up we started to have some blistering rows. When I reached twenty and started to work abroad, it was a very useful safety valve. Paddy could indulge himself in his rituals of daily living while I was away, and I had the opportunity to please myself. Most repats I threatened to move out permanently, but by that time we'd moved into the bay, and I love it here, so——'

'Was your father never tempted to marry again?'

'Hell no! He had our lives so finely turned that no way could he have coped with an outsider. Whenever I invited friends home he hated every minute. He was on edge in case they set down glasses on the furniture, or left fingermarks.' Chase grimaced. 'Julia was a perpetual thorn in his flesh, but I made a point of taking her home because it *was* my home. He might have been happy to live like a monk, but I damn well wasn't! If Paddy had had his way, we'd have been

a couple of sanitised hermits.' He grew thoughtful, a hand rubbing his jaw. 'Even so, I guess it
was kind of a selfish existence. Most of what we
did was to suit ourselves. I suppose you could call
it one long ego trip.'

'Trap not trip,' Romy corrected. 'You don't
strike me as being full of your own importance.'

'Thank you, ma'am,' he tossed in, but she had
not finished.

'Though sometimes it does seem as if you live
in a cage, a luxurious orderly cage, where
anything out of the ordinary upsets you.'

He arched a brow. 'Just because I don't like
dried seaweed? You haven't enrolled at Ginette's
psycho-analysis workshop have you, Miss Freud?'

She laughed. 'No, I'm self-taught. And to be
honest, I didn't think that much of the seaweed,
either.' She patted the papers. 'So why don't you
take this list away, tot up the totals and let me
know if it meets with your approval?'

'Must I? I'd rather stay here. It feels good,
talking to you like this, telling you the intimate
details of my past.' He grinned mischeviously.
'You wouldn't like to hear about my sex life,
would you?'

Romy's heart began to pump. There had to be
more affairs than just Julia, but if he told her
about the other women who had lain in his arms,
he would be halfway to crucifying her. She shook
her head.

'I'd rather we skipped that and you went home.
I have things to do.'

Chase pushed back his chair from the table. He
stood up, hands in his pockets, and slouched,
pelvis slightly forward, watching her. The air was
heavy. His eyes were brooding, wandering,

lingering over her breasts and hips, and up again
to her mouth.

'Such as?' he queried.

'Don't look at me like that,' she implored. His
smoky blue gaze was hypnotising her, making her
think of only one thing—she and Chase together,
lying together, naked together, joined together . . .

'Like what?' he drawled.

Romy felt weak with longing, but she, too,
pushed herself to her feet, the chair scraping on
the wooden floor. 'Like, like——' Her arms
arced and dipped, copying a graceful Balinese
dancer.

He took a step forward, reaching out to clasp
her shoulders, pulling her against him. He bent
his dark head. 'Like I want to make love to you?
But I do. Romy,' he said, against her mouth.
'Romy.' He said her name like a plea, and then he
kissed her. The kiss was deep and satisfying, and
when it ended and she looked into his face, Romy
saw Chase was as disturbed as she was. 'I swear
I've never felt so involved with any one before,'
he said huskily. 'Stay here, baby, please. Give us
a chance to develop, room to breathe.'

'No.' The word was a sob, and she felt his
fingers spread across her shoulder blades. Hard
long fingers, taut with frustration and suppressed
emotion.

'I won't let you down,' he growled, deep in his
throat.

Romy gasped in air to help her form the words.
'Won't you?' She pushed out of his grasp,
moving a yard away in a need to be free, free of
his touch, free of the desire which was threatening
to devour her. 'Okay, I accept that in a weird sort
of way you're an honourable man, but we're

starting off from two entirely different concepts. I can't afford to become involved with you.' She took a deep breath. 'When I bleed, Chase, it's blood that comes out.'

'And you think I don't bleed?' he demanded roughly.

'No. To be honest, I don't think that in thirty-five years you ever have.' She thrust the inventory at him. 'So just go home, *now*.'

She set the alarm to ring early next morning. On waking, Romy donned the tattered silver suit and ate a bowl of muesli, before emerging into the sunshine. Today she was prepared for her final battle with Mother Nature.

Hour after hour she worked, tugging up weeds, chopping down thickets, pruning bushes until they were no more than a few tiny sticks poking out of the sandy earth. The pile of dead rubbish grew until it loomed like the Empire State Building, yet despite all her efforts only a third of the ground, at most, had been cleared when the sun turned to orange-gold and began its descent. Romy wondered why she had bothered. If the garden was left alone, a fresh crop of luxuriant growth would rapidly replace all she had razed, and with Chase in his present mood anything, or nothing, could happen to the little cabin and its plot of land.

Why must he falter in his determination now? They appeared to have switched roles, or was it that neither of them was what the other had first imagined? During all the weeks she had known him, Chase had invariably planned ahead, always been decisive, yet now he was vague. It was Romy who had a clear picture of what came

next—a flight back to England, time at her
father's apartment while she found employment
and then, if Chase's money would stretch that
far, she would look for a tiny pied-à-terre of her
own in London.

A final branch was chopped in two and flung
on to the bonfire. Wiping the sweat from her
brow, Romy stored away her tools and went into
the house to find matches. Only when she
reached the kitchen did she realise she was
hungry, so the bonfire was temporarily suspended
while she made a plate of scrambled eggs.

It was twilight when she came out again, and
the bay was steeped in dark grey, a grey which
gauzed the distant outline of the cliffs, softened
the rocks into a ragged tumble across the sand.
Everything was tranquil. Even the sea had
quietened, the water now rolling where it had
danced, pulling and surging without a sound. In
the fading light she once again felt as if she was
the single soul on earth. If Chase was keeping
track of her progress from his eyrie on the hill,
she no longer cared. Nothing mattered. Her time
in California had ended. Now was farewell.
Farewell to the bay she had grown to love.
Farewell to Chase O'Donoghue who cared too
little.

Romy struck a match and tossed it forward,
watching the flame catch at the dead straw.
Within seconds the bonfire was ablaze, the tinder
dry mass flaring and crackling, sparks flying high
into the night air. She gazed deep into the
melting heart of crimson and yellow-gold, and
the fire took on a character of its own. It was her
master, demanding and receiving her homage as
she circled, searching for sacrifices of wood and

dead foliage which it greedily devoured, always
needing more. Moving about in the dusk with the
heat of the fire on her face, Romy became
involved in a pagan ritual. The fire god was
supreme. Fire cleansed and sterilised. Where
once had been a huge pile of branches and dried
grass, tomorrow there would be ashes. Ashes.
Her love for Chase was in ashes. She stood, her
hands pressed against flushed cheeks, staring into
the flames.

Some crazy impulse made her bend to tug off
her battered shoes from China and fling them
into the red inferno, laughing as the fire god
gobbled up her sacrifice. Barefoot, Romy watched
the shoes disappear until only slender black bones
remained. Her laughter changed to melancholy.
Stretching out her arms, Romy's eyelids closed as
she wished and wished that things could have
been different. But she was a girl in a silver suit,
and Chase . . .

'Oh, Chase!' A ragged sob escaped, startling
her. There would be no more Chase, and no more
girl in a silver suit. Oblivious of the cool of the
evening, Romy caught at the tab at her neck and,
with a dramatic gesture of farewell, ripped down
the zip and stepped free of the voluminous silver
embrace. Naked now, she rolled the torn and
tattered cloth-of-silver into a parcel and offered it
to the flames. A strange silvery-blue flare
shimmered, rising and swaying from the shiny
folds to make an exotic pattern which entranced
her. Arms wrapped around her glowing body,
Romy basked in the fire's heat and watched as the
silver suit twisted and writhed, dying gracefully.
Only when tears dripped on to her breasts, did
she realise she was crying.

'I loved you, silver suit,' she exclaimed out loud, plighting her troth. 'And I loved you, Chase.'

'But I *love you*, Romy.'

Her hand flew to her mouth. Now she was hearing voices. She *was* an oddball, just like Great-aunt Prudence. She had been on her own far too long, or was it the fire which had hypnotised her into believing she had heard those words she had dreamed of hearing? She gazed into the dying embers. The silver suit had disappeared and only a ghostly outline remained, a blue glow dancing above a silver sheen.

The deep voice came again out of the night. 'I love you, Romy. We belong together, both of us here at the bay. Will you marry me?'

Blinking as her eyes adjusted to the darkness, she turned and made out a tall figure standing on the far side of the fence.

'Chase!' she said weakly.

He swooped over the fence like a jungle cat, and held out his arms. Unthinking, acting instinctively, Romy went into them.

'Marry me,' he implored, holding her close. 'The bay, the diving ranch, my whole life means nothing if you're not here to share it with me.'

Murmuring her assent, Romy wrapped her slender arms around his neck, arching as his caressing mouth covered hers, and then moved on to kiss her face, her throat, her shoulders. Crushed against his strong body, she knew this was where she belonged. Now the pulsating heat came from within and though, for a while it did not occur to either of them that she was naked in his arms, gradually his hands were compelled into a fevered path, cupping her breasts and feeling the gentle swoop of her spine. 'Let's go,' he commanded huskily, swinging her up into his arms. He glanced down at the glowing remains. 'The fire has nearly died.'

'But the fire's *inside* me,' she whispered, clinging to him as he covered the route to the cabin in long strides.

'And inside me, too.' Chase set her down on the verandah. 'Find some clothes. Don't get cold, baby. We'll go up to my place and you can have a hot toddy and a dip in the tub to chase away any chills.

The water felt warm and silky. Naked once more, Romy slid down into the circular tub until her hips nudged the seat. She relaxed, arms resting on the padded surround, as she abandoned herself to the buoyancy until she felt she was floating. Water flapped at her breasts, sensually stroking the rosy pinnacles until they firmed.

'Your whisky toddy, ma'am,' Chase grinned, striding in with only a towel suspended at his hips. He set two steaming tumblers on the golden tiles, the towel dropped, and he slid downwards to join her. Romy took a hurried gulp of the fiery liquid. Once before she had thought how at home he was in the water, and now he was totally at ease, seeming careless of the fact that they were both naked. He lifted his glass in a toast. 'To beautiful girls who perform delectable stripteases before bonfires! If we ever get short of customers at the diving ranch, we could always advertise you as an added attraction!'

'No way,' she protested, flicking reprimanding fingers in the water and making him jerk aside. He laughed, and shook diamond droplets out of his hair. 'I thought you were having doubts about the ranch?' Romy said, taking another gulp of hot toddy.

'Not any longer. At one stage I couldn't see how I was going to continue living at the bay once you'd left, but now, with Mrs O'Donoghue at my side, I have a wonderful feeling that everything will be fine.' He moved closer along the seat until his thigh brushed against the soft bareness of her hip. 'You realise we've done this all wrong?'

'Done what all wrong?' His nearness was making it increasingly difficult to think straight. She had never been naked with a man before, and this one was so damned gorgeous that she could hardly breathe!

'The hot tub bit. Shouldn't I have covered you with mayonnaise? Or was it Thousand Island dressing?'

Romy grinned. 'That's before you throw me into the snow, not the hot water.' Somehow it was impossible to keep her eyes from the tanned stretch of his shoulders above the water, and the rest of him below. Her fingers were tingling with the compulsion to touch him.

'We could work a variation. We'll do it next time,' he decided, and had a gulp of the whisky.

'You're not serious?' She could not determine if he was joking. This mercurial maverick was not at all like the solemn layer-down-of-the-law she had first encountered. 'You can't!' she cried. 'The water will be horribly greasy and we'll slip on the tiles, and the smell will hang around for days. You'll probably clog up the drains, too.'

'So what's the big panic about a few clogged drains?'

'I don't know,' she said weakly. Romy felt lightheaded, though whether from the effect of the warm water and her whisky drink, or the hard stretch of the male body beside her, she could not tell. 'Why did you decide to come down to the cabin and play the role of Peeping Tom?' she questioned, taking another rapid swallow. She pinned her eyes to his face, determined not to be led astray. Now she knew that Chase was *all* Greek god, from the top of his curly head all the way down to his toes, and the realisation did her composure no good at all.

'I didn't, I came prepared to fire-fight.' He drained his glass, pushing it away across the tiles. 'The flames were visible from my patio and I convinced myself you were destined to set everything alight, cabin and all. I had visions of a massive inferno.'

Careless of her hair dripping into the water, Romy tilted her head. 'Instead of which, I had everything under control.'

'Did you? You standing there as naked as the day you were born, sobbing out your heart, didn't seem much like control.'

'Well, maybe not,' she agreed.

'And speaking of control, do you think you could hurry up and finish that?' he asked, gesturing towards the final inch of golden liquid in her glass. 'I only have a certain amount, and with the sight of you like that it's being used up at a dramatic rate.'

Chase curved his fingers into her hair to cup the back of her head and pull her close. When her lips parted at the behest of his probing tongue. Romy was immediately adrift in a sea of desire. His kisses became deeper, urgent, and his hands

claimed her breasts, massaging beneath the water
until her nipples hardened even more in his
palms and Romy began to whimper. The swirl of
silky water around them was an erotic stimulant
and as their bodies swayed, gliding and rubbing,
naked skin on naked skin, she, too, allowed her
hands to explore.

'*God!*' Chase groaned. He moved, lifting her on
to him until she felt the thrust of his hips and was so
violently, so totally aroused that she was hardly
aware of him carrying her from the tub to his bed.
With impassioned haste, Chase dabbed them both
semi-dry, leaving the heat from their bodies to do
the rest, and then lay down beside her. His body
felt hard and hot and slippery, and she sighed,
running her hands over his shoulders, his chest, the
narrowness of his waist, the throbbing muscles of
his thighs. 'Oh baby, I knew you'd be good,' he
whispered as she pleasured him and then,
discovering hidden reserves of control, he began to
school her in the ways of desire, responding to her
need to touch and be touched, to give and receive.
He knew she held nothing back, that she responded
fully, naturally and for the first time he, too, gave
and gave, until everything else melted away and
they were alone in the universe, a man and a
woman. When he bent his dark head to her breasts
she shuddered, loving the rub of his lips across the
swollen contours, and when he caught a jutting
nipple between his teeth, she cried out in soft
delight. Romy moved closer into him. She was
burning, consumed by the fire which was Chase,
his flames licking over her body, sending sparks
circling in her head, turning her blood to molten
gold. She moved restlessly in his arms, eager and
yet frightened.

'Don't be afraid, I won't hurt you,' he assured her huskily. 'I love you.'

His hands slid downwards, stroking until the blood sang in her ears and she was damp with desire. Chase moved slowly and firmly, holding her as the passion built, until the last thread of his control snapped and he was thrusting inside her. Romy cried out again, but the moment of pain was forgotten as he took her onwards, moving rhythmically within her until she was gasping, body arched, her fingers clutching at his shoulders, the nails biting into his tanned flesh.

'Romy!' he cried, and a sensation of volcanic release rocked them both into oblivion.

Afterwards they lay together at peace, their bodies dried by the fire of their love. Chase kissed her shoulder, a shoulder which felt warm to his lips.

'I never realised being in love was like this,' he said wonderingly, and when Romy raised her green eyes, he grinned. 'I'd dismissed it as so much make believe, but it's goddamn wonderful.'

'And you only took thirty-five years to work that out,' she teased.

'So, I'm a late starter,' he chuckled, his hand moving to caress the firm fullness of her breast. 'Which sounds like one helluva good excuse for making up for lost time. Shall we?'

'Maybe it would be wise to tackle your yard today, while I still have some slight reserves of strength,' Chase remarked at breakfast the following morning. 'A few more nights like last night, and there's a distinct possibility I shall be permanently on crutches.' He grinned, holding her hand across the table. 'But first I must cable

the Middle East and tell them I'm terminating
my contract.'

'Isn't there one last trip planned?' Romy asked.

'You don't think I'm going to leave you here in
the bay alone, do you? Besides, I have better
things to do right now than sink to the ocean
floor—like getting married for example.' He
grinned, then sobered so that Romy could see
him making preparations in his head. 'This
morning we must telephone your father and
break the news.'

'And telephone Ginette?' she asked, with a
sidelong glance.

Chase gave a mock shudder. 'She'll have to
know sometime, but not today.' A vagrant
thought wandered into his head, and his face fell.
'I'd forgotten, you've burned your silver suit.
What'll you wear for working in now?'

'I could go into San Francisco and buy denim
dungarees.'

He shook his head. 'That's too ordinary for my
girl.'

'But I *am* ordinary,' she protested.

He came round the table to gather her up in his
arms. 'Romy, my love, you are anything but
ordinary. Divine, certainly, and exciting and
beautiful and funny and——' His mouth covered
hers. 'But *not* ordinary,' he said at last.

She pressed her fingertips across his mouth to
stop a second kiss, making Chase content himself
by nibbling at her fingers. 'So what do you
suggest I wear?' she asked.

He thought a minute, then he grinned. 'How
about those satin shorts and the boob tube?'

'They're not very suitable for gardening,' she
protested.

He pulled her fingers away in order that his mouth could plunder at will. 'No, but they're very sexy, and easy to remove,' he murmured, after a kiss which had her head spinning.

'Aren't you saving your strength for dealing with the undergrowth?' she protested, as his mouth departed on an erotic path along her throat.

'To hell with the undergrowth. I can think of a much more satisfying way of making me as weak as a kitten. Come back to bed and I'll show you.

That morning the bay was silent. The sun shone and a gentle breeze whispered through the grassy meadows. Caught amidst a thicket, a lone sliver of silver cloth danced and shone, and three days later a tall, curly-headed man discovered it. Now the silver strand is tucked in his wallet and lies next to his heart.

ROMANCE

Next month's romances from Mills & Boon

Each month, you can choose from a world of variety in romance with Mills & Boon. These are the new titles to look out for next month.

RULES OF THE GAME Penny Jordan
AN UNWILLING DESIRE Carole Mortimer
FACADE Jessica Steele
A TIME TO GROW Claudia Jameson
LOVE'S TANGLED WEB Mary Lyons
ISLAND OF DOLPHINS Lilian Cheatham
OUT OF THIS DARKNESS Madeleine Ker
FLASHBACK Amanda Carpenter
PERSONAL VENDETTA Margaret Mayo
FALLEN IDOL Margaret Way
MEGAN'S FOLLY Maura McGiveny
NUMBER ONE Donna Huxley

Buy them from your usual paperback stockist, or write to: Mills & Boon Reader Service, P.O. Box 236, Thornton Rd, Croydon, Surrey CR9 3RU, England. Readers in South Africa-write to: Mills & Boon Reader Service of Southern Africa, Private Bag X3010, Randburg, 2125.

Mills & Boon
the rose of romance

Take 4
Exciting Books
Absolutely
FREE

Love, romance, intrigue... all are captured for you by
Mills & Boon's top-selling authors. By becoming a
regular reader of Mills & Boon's Romances you can
enjoy 6 superb new titles every month plus a whole
range of special benefits: your very own personal
membership card, a free monthly newsletter packed
with recipes, competitions, exclusive book offers and
a monthly guide to the stars, plus extra bargain offers
and big cash savings.

AND an Introductory FREE GIFT for YOU.
Turn over the page for details.

As a special introduction we will send you four exciting **Mills & Boon Romances Free** and without obligation when you complete and return this coupon.

At the same time we will reserve a subscription to Mills & Boon Reader Service for you. Every month, you will receive 6 of the very latest novels by leading Romantic Fiction authors, delivered direct to your door. You don't pay extra for delivery — postage and packing is always completely Free. There is no obligation or commitment — you can cancel your subscription at any time.

You have nothing to lose and a whole world of romance to gain.

Just fill in and post the coupon today to **MILLS & BOON READER SERVICE, FREEPOST, P.O. BOX 236, CROYDON, SURREY CR9 9EL.**

Please Note:- READERS IN SOUTH AFRICA write to Mills & Boon, Postbag X3010, Randburg 2125, S. Africa.

- -

FREE BOOKS CERTIFICATE

To: Mills & Boon Reader Service, FREEPOST, P.O. Box 236, Croydon, Surrey CR9 9EL.

Please send me, free and without obligation, four Mills & Boon Romances, and reserve a Reader Service Subscription for me. If I decide to subscribe I shall, from the beginning of the month following my free parcel of books, receive six new books each month for £6.60, post and packing free. If I decide not to subscribe, I shall write to you within 10 days. The free books are mine to keep in any case. I understand that I may cancel my subscription at any time simply by writing to you. I am over 18 years of age.

Please write in BLOCK CAPITALS.

Signature _____

Name _____

Address _____

_____ Post code _____

SEND NO MONEY — TAKE NO RISKS.

Please don't forget to include your Postcode.

6R   *Offer expires December 31st 1984*

EP86